MARINE ENGINEERING DESIGN AND INSTALLATION SERIES

MARINE GEARING

A descriptive review of marine gearing, the problems and their solution. The evolution to meet modern power requirements and ship conditions. Some basic fundamentals

by

J. F. SHANNON, Ph.D., B.Sc., C.Eng., F.I.Mech.E., M.I.E.S.

formerly Chief Engineer, Experimental Development and Gearing Departments AEI (now GEC) and Consultant. Formerly Member of NAVGRA Technical Committee

D1612821

THE INSTITUT... ...RS

Published for the Institute of Marine Engineers

by

Marine Media Management Ltd.
76 Mark Lane, London EC3R 7JN
(England Reg. No. 1100685)

ISBN : 0 900976 67 5

Printed in Great Britain by The Eastern Press Ltd.,
London and Reading

CONTENTS

Acknowledgements

This review has been made possible by the courtesy of the firms and authors who have supplied photographs and papers.

To them, the author expresses his thanks and appreciation.

So also with appropriate matter taken from the *Transactions* of Institutions and other technical literature, references are given, which together frame the subject.

It is hoped that seagoing engineers, superintendents and others, for whom this review was primarily written, will benefit, and in their study of the data from practice and in their appraisal of new machinery, will encourage progress which gives greater reliability and efficiency.

It is hoped also that the research worker, design and development engineer will appreciate better the problems, and bridge any gap between the laboratory, test bed and sea experience.

CONVERSION TABLE—S.I. UNITS

Power:
  1 hp = 0·7457 kW

Stress and Pressure:
  1 lbf/in² = 0·703 kgf/cm² = 6·895 kN/m²
  1 kgf/cm² = 14·2233 lbf/in² = 98·0662 kN/m²

Length:
  1 inch = 25·4 mm
  1 mil (thou) = 25·4μm
  1 micro-inch (μ in) = 10^{-6} in = 25·4 nm
  1 mm = 0·0394 in = 39·4 mil (thou)

  1 μm (micron) = 0·0394 mil (thou)

INTRODUCTION

Progress in modern marine gearing has shown many advances which could be listed as follows:

(a) Accuracy of gear cutting and gear grinding, giving exact involute tooth form and good surface finish with corrections by shaving and grinding.

(b) The progress on gear tooth materials, from nickel steel pinions and carbon steel wheel rims to through-hardened alloy steel combinations, known as " soft on soft " followed by surface-hardened gears—" hard on hard "—and a combination of surface-hardened pinions on " soft " wheel rims as an intermediate stage " hard on soft ".

(c) The full scale testing and development of these materials by naval-industrial organisations gave a great advance in tooth loading and reliability, and the introduction of combination machinery, steam and gas turbines, with their necessary automatic clutches, led to the development of large reversing gears and the alternative large power c.p. propeller.

(d) The problem of shaft alignment in large and more flexible ships, with larger powers at lower revolutions with shorter and stiffer shafts, requires the use of 3D finite-element analysis of the aft end of the ship's structure and the seating for the engines, gearing and thrust block, to obtain the best design and optimum setting for the shaft bearings. The aim is to get about equal loads on the fore and after main wheel bearings, which is a basic requirement for the internal alignment of the gears.

(e) Solutions to this apparently incompatible situation of the flexible ship and the stiff intermediate short shafts are the use of flexible cardan shaft couplings, flexible centre drive disc in the main wheel, flexible mounting of the gearcase or gearcase/engine assembly.

The internal alignment is maintained by symmetrical design or rigid gearcases on 3–4 point supports.

(f) The requirements of low head room are met by different configurations of gearing, e.g. locked-train arrangements, the introduction of epicyclic gearing in the first reduction and in the second reduction in conjunction with parallel gearing for multiple engines. For very low speeds, triple-reduction gears are used either as locked-train arrangements or as epicyclic-parallel shaft gears.

(g) Neat solutions are available for geared diesel drives with epicyclic gears for single engines and parallel shaft gears for multiple engines. Various methods are used for reversing.

1

(h) In detail, developments have taken place in lubricating oil systems, bearing design, vibration analysis, noise and in the role of lubrication in involute tooth action, and in understanding the mechanism of pitting and scuffing, so that these are no longer major problems in modern gearing.

1. HISTORY AND DEVELOPMENT OF GEAR-HOBBING MACHINES AND REFERENCE TO GEAR-GRINDING MACHINES

The first gearing for marine propulsion was a double-helical, double reduction gear, evolved by de Laval in 1889 for his 15 hp turbine, geared from 16 000 rev/min to 330 rev/min.[1] Thus gearing became the medium permitting the turbine and propeller to function at their optimum speeds.

This was followed up by the de Laval Company in U.S.A. who started building a high quality hobbing machine.[1] Others followed and thus began a universal endeavour to manufacture accurate gears. The first large high speed gear to be used in service was that installed in the s.s. *Vespanian* by the Parsons Marine Steam Turbine Company in 1910.[2]

FIG. 1.1.—Turbine Gear-Hobbing Machine showing gear being hobbed. Ref. G.E.C.(U.K.). The three essential motions of a gear-hobbing machine (i) the rotation of the work table; (ii) the rotation of the hob and (iii) the linear traverse of the hob saddle, must be correct in themselves and in relation to each other. (Timms).

3

In the 1910–20 period, gearing was a formidable problem, the troubles being mainly due to poor gear cutting, giving undulations which, with misalignment, gave rise to pitting and wear on the teeth, scuffing and scoring, gear noise and tooth breakage.

Sir Charles Parsons [3] recognised that the cyclic errors in the dividing wheel of the gear cutting machine caused high spots on the tooth profile of helical teeth, inclined to the tooth tip at the same angle as the contact line between the mating gears, and that this was the worst condition for noise. The frequency of the disturbance corresponded to the number of teeth in the dividing wheel.

FIG. 1.2.—Meshing of secondary pinion and main wheel. Minor refinements can be made if required by the gear shaving process, the final correction being assessed by the contact marking between the mating gears. With a brake on the cutter spindle, selective shaving can be applied on one side of the teeth only. (G.E.C.(U.K.)).

This led to the Parsons " creep table " drive on the hobbing machine which redistributed the high spots caused by the periodic errors of the worm and worm-wheel drive of the hobbing machine, spirally around the gear being cut.[3, 4, 5] However, dispersal of the errors was not enough: their elimination or reduction was required.

World events in 1914–18 intervened in these developments; nevertheless in the U.S.A., several firms—de Laval, G.E., and Westinghouse—with high quality hobbing machines, were able to build successful double-reduction gearing. Most other manufacturers had trouble with such gearing and confined themselves to single-reduction designs. Double-reduction gearing for turbine driven merchant ships at that time was of the articulated types and interleaved designs with either split secondaries or split primaries (Figs. 7.1, 7.2, 7.3 and 7.4).

Apart from gear tooth errors, other troubles occurred such as torsional vibration of the propeller, shafting, gears and turbines. These were solved in some cases by tuning the system to give a node at the gear, thereby at least eliminating " gear hammer ". To overcome tooth troubles, all addendum (AA) and Vickers-Bostock-Bramley (VBB) tooth forms were introduced, but the chief problem of inaccuracies in gear cutting remained. The cumulative pitch errors on wheels were of the order of 5×10^{-3} in (125 μm) whereas today $< 5 \times 10^{-4}$ in (12·5 μm) is required. This was having a remarkable effect on the marine turbine industry as has been described vividly by Dr. A. W. Davis in his Parsons Memorial Lecture 1974.[2]

FIG. 1.3.—Universal hob saddle of a Pfauter Hobbing Machine with a helical gear in the course of hobbing.
The hob is inclined at an angle which brings the thread parallel to the tooth spiral of the gear to be generated. The hob is in the form of a worm having an involute thread that has been fluted and relieved to provide cutting edges which remain as part of the surface of an involute helicoid. The hob is rotated at a suitable cutting speed and the blank is rotated at a speed which the finished gear would have to mesh with a worm rotating at the speed of the hob.

Towards 1939, the articulated locked-train, double-helical gear was adopted by the U.S. Navy to increase the power/weight ratio (Figs. 7–10). This was achieved with very high quality hobbing machines which gave good surface finish and accuracy. Later, in the U.K., with a target of accuracy set by the Admiralty, expressed in B.S. 1498—" Gear hobbing machines for turbine and similar drives ",

Fig. 1.4.—Base of a Schiess gear hobbing machine.

Fig. 1.4a.—Work table base.

Fig. 1.4b.—Part of master worm wheel. The annular steep angle tapered table track and the large number of teeth in the worm wheel are to be noted.

Fig. 1.5.—G.E.C. pinion shaving machine with electrically controlled brake and system for selective shaving.

FIG. 1.6.—G.E.C. pinion shaving machine showing shaving cutter. The helix angle of the cutter teeth is made so that the cutter will mesh with the gear with their axes at an angle of 10° to 15°.

followed by B.S. 1807 covering turbine gears, the large steam turbine and gear firms with research facilities together with the Metrology Dept [4] of the National Physical Laboratory pursued the search for accuracy in gear manufacture.

This led to the development of master worm and worm-wheels with a larger number of teeth, 500 to 1000 to give constant rotation of the work table and to bring the high spots of the much reduced periodic errors within the consecutive cuts of the hob, thereby reducing their effect. Also accurate lead screws were developed giving accurate linear traverse of the hob saddle and rotation of the hob. Thus, with a large number of cutting edges on the hob and a fine feed of the hob per revolution of the work, the deviations of the enveloping cuts from the theoretical involute were practically negligible and gave a good surface finish—Figs. 1.1, 1.2, 1.3, 1.4.[6, 7, 8, 9, 10, 11]

The post hobbing process of shaving on material of < 70 tons/in² UTS is used to improve the surface still further and to modify the tooth profile to ensure smooth and uniform meshing of the mating teeth (Figs. 1.5, 1.6). The helix angle can also be modified where necessary to compensate for pinion distortion due to bending and torsion under load so that nearly uniform full face meshings takes place under full load. Such modifications are very small but are extremely important. Surface finishes of 10–20 μ-inch (micro-inch) C.L.A. (centre-line average) by grinding, 15–30 μ-inch by shaving and 25–40 μ-inch by hobbing are obtained as standard.[104, 105]

The CLA height of a surface is defined as the arithmetical average departure of the profile, both above and below its centre line, throughout a short prescribed sample length. Values are expressed in micro-inches (10^{-6} inch) CLA and surface finish readings are taken on a Talysurf-type recording instrument.

Fig. 1.7.—N.E.L. portable diffraction grating unit mounted on the hob spindle and work table of a 150 inch gear-hobbing machine (G.E.C.(U.K.)). The basic system of accuracy is $\pm\,0\cdot4$ seconds of arc. Skilful correction was taken to a total amplitude of error less than 3 seconds of arc, as shown in Fig. 1.8.

The equipment is also used on gear grinding machines. (Smith, N.E.L.).

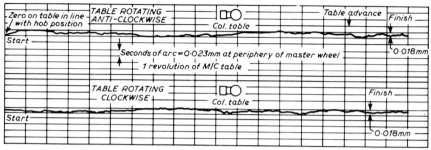

Proc. Instn Mech Engrs 1969-70

FIG. 1.8.—Final records of hobbing machine correction. This is about a third of the error permitted for a Class A1 gear. B.S. 1807. " Gears for turbine and similar drives."

The successful use of shaving depends largely on the original accuracy of the hobbing process, as no amount of shaving will make a badly cut gear into a good one.

Hobbing machines must be of rigid construction and supported on resilient mountings to ensure isolation from external influences and they must be enclosed in a temperature controlled cell or building maintained to $\pm$ 1°F and temperature of the oil and cutting fluid controlled to ensure thermal stability.

With the ever improving methods of measurement, from smoked glass instruments to laser interferometers, the extremely high accuracy required of the

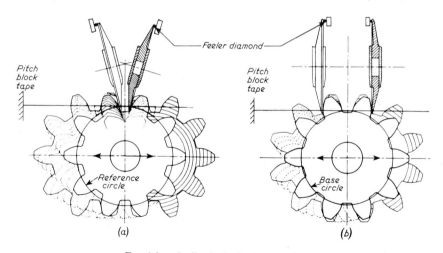

FIG. 1.9a.—Inclined wheel grinding method.
Grinding wheels inclined at the pressure angle and the pitch block tape set at a corresponding reference circle.
FIG. 1.9b.—Zero degree grinding method and grinding generating circles.
The pitch block tape coincides with the base circle where the pressure angle is zero. The generating motion is obtained by rolling on the base circle.
FIG. 1.9.—Gear-grinding by oscillating rolling-generating motion. (MAAG).

Fig. 1.10.—MAAG gear-grinding machine HSS-90S capable of grinding pinions and wheels up to 35·5 inch (0·9 m) in diameter.

hobbing machine can be maintained with skilful correction. Figs. 1.7 and 1.8, show the final records of a 150-inch hobbing machine after skilful correction. The double amplitude of the fundamental components of error is less than three seconds of arc which is within the B.S. 1498 Grade A Standard.[13] The laser and other high class instruments can detect an angular movement of 0·5 sec of arc, 0·00025 in (6 μm) at 100 inches (2·5 m) radius.

Machines are availables which give the high standard of accuracy required. As an example the 1968 Schiess 230-inch hobbing machine is quoted as giving a cumulative pitch error (once per revolution of the wheel) of one second of arc. Similar high accuracies are obtained with the MAAG gear-grinding machines, which have led to the use of hardened and ground gears.[12]

Gear-grinding is a more accurate process than shaving, and it can be applied to heat-treated as well as case-hardened gears. The final accuracy is independent of the pre-grinding process. The MAAG method of gear-grinding is by generation. The blank is given an oscillating rolling motion so that two dished grinding wheels, set at the spiral angle, generate two sides of the involute teeth. Fig. 1.9 shows the grinding wheels at two different settings.

In the latest zero method of grinding used on MAAG machines, the two grinding wheels rotate in planes parallel to each other and grind the tooth flanks

FIG. 1.11.—The MAAG gear-grinding machine HSS-360, which can accommodate gears up to 142 inches (3·6 m) in diameter, being prepared for grinding a final reduction gearwheel.

with their inner edges. Since the grinding pressure angle and the base circle pressure angle are both zero, the generating motion is obtained by rolling on the base circle. The feed stroke by this method gives a gap of normal width between the helices when grinding double-helical gears.

These machines have cam arrangements for making the involute and longitudinal corrections required for highly loaded high speed gears.[12]

Fig. 1.10 shows the MAAG gear grinder Type HSS.90S capable of grinding pinions up to 35·5 in (0·9 m) in diameter. Fig. 1.11 shows the MAAG gear grinder Type HSS.360 which can accommodate gears up to 142 inches (3·6 m) in diameter, being prepared for grinding a final reduction wheel.

Such machines have made possible the notable step forward in gearing, giving the highest standards necessary to achieve higher loadings with greater reliability and quietness in operation.

2. TOOTH LOADING AND DISTRIBUTION CORRECTIONS

When a pinion, with uniform meshing at no load, is torqued at one end, it bends and twists, giving an algebraically combined deflection as shown in Fig. 2.1. The load distribution is proportional to the tooth deflection and is obtained as shown in Figs. 2.1a, b, c and d.[14]

From this new load distribution, new bending and twisting deflections can be obtained from which a corrected load distribution follows, giving in turn, its corresponding combined deflection. Such calculations can be carried out graphically or numerically by computer, accounting for helix correction, alignment, bearing flexibility and thermal effects.

An uncertain factor in the calculations is the tooth stiffness S. For a normal pressure angle of 20° Davis[16] gave $S = 4000$ and 3000 lb/in per $0 \cdot 001$ inch for helix angles of 15° and 30° respectively; these values are used in Fig. 2.1d for the single-helical and double-helical pinions. Other workers give S approximately half the above values. In view of this uncertainty and the effects of journal yielding to unequal loads, the fairly accurate deflections from the first approximations (Fig. 2.1c) are taken as a guide to the helix corrections and alignment required.

The maximum tangential deflections δ_{max} at the torqued end, divided by the mean load per inch of tooth face W_{IF} is a unique function of the face-width/diameter ratio F/d as shown in Fig. 2.2 for single and double-helical gears.

This deflection is absorbed by the combined flexibility of the teeth and gives the relationship between the " maximum local load per inch " W_{max} and " mean load per inch " W_{if} as a function of F/d and the flexibility of the teeth.

Expressed in terms of Lloyd's K factor, $\dfrac{W_{if}}{d} \dfrac{(r+1)}{r}$,* it follows that the ratio of the mean K loading, to the maximum local K_{max} is a unique function of F/d and the flexibility of the teeth. Fig. 2.3 shows the relationship between K/K_{max} and F/d for various tooth flexibilities.[16 and 17]

Also since $\dfrac{HP}{n} = K \dfrac{F}{d} d^3 \times \dfrac{8}{10^6} \dfrac{r}{r+1}$ where $\dfrac{HP}{n}$ = torque number and r is the gear ratio for the mesh, the optimum value of $K \dfrac{F}{d}$ and therefore $\dfrac{HP}{n}$ for a

* Lloyd's K factor—Chapter 4, p. 23.

12

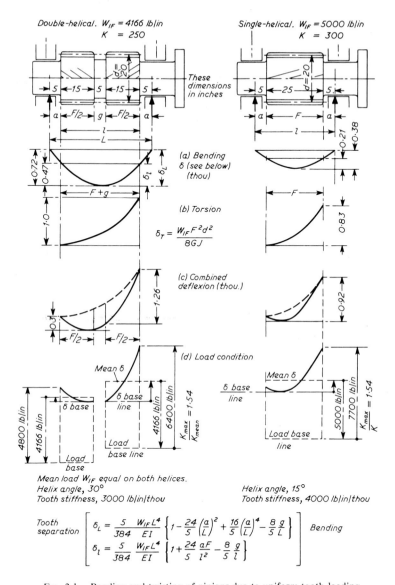

FIG. 2.1.—Bending and twisting of pinions due to uniform tooth loading.

pinion diameter is obtained by plotting $K \dfrac{F}{d} \div K_{max}$ as shown on Fig. 2.3. This occurs over a range of F/d values of $1\cdot5$ to $2\cdot0$.

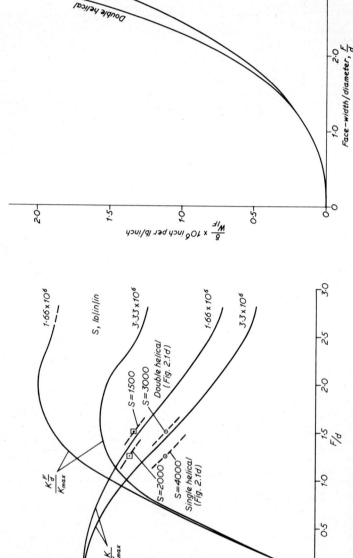

Fig. 2.2.—Maximum tangential tooth separations, due to bending and twisting of pinion for an average tooth load W_{if} lb/inch.

Fig. 2.3.—Relationship between Lloyd's K factor and face-width/diameter for different tooth flexibilities.

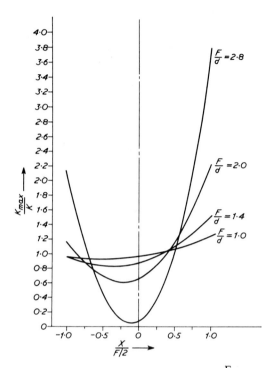

Fig. 2.4.—Distribution of load across face of pinion with different $\dfrac{F}{d}$ ratios for tooth flexibility.

$S = 3 \cdot 3 \times 10^6$ lb/in/in. (Weber & Banaschek).

For higher average K values smaller F/d ratios must be used, otherwise the corrections would be too severe. Fig. 2.4 shows the distribution of load across the face of a single-helical pinion with different F/d, ratios for a tooth stiffness $S = 3 \cdot 3 \times 10^6$ lb/in per inch as calculated by Weber and Banaschek.[15] Fig. 2.3 is an associated diagram giving the maximum values. On a similar basis Figs. 2.5a, b and c taken from Kerpestein [22] show the load distribution curves illustrating the effects of " helix " correction, misalignment and differential temperature between pinion and wheel.

TEMPERATURE EFFECTS
    Usually the temperature of the pinion is higher than that of the main wheel and if uniformly heated, all dimensions will increase and there will be a change in base pitch and axial pitch.
    The change in axial pitch is most important as this loads the teeth at one end of the helix. With apex trailing, the teeth bear hard on the inner ends and with apex leading the teeth bear hard on the outer ends. Fig. 2.5c shows apex trailing to be advantageous.

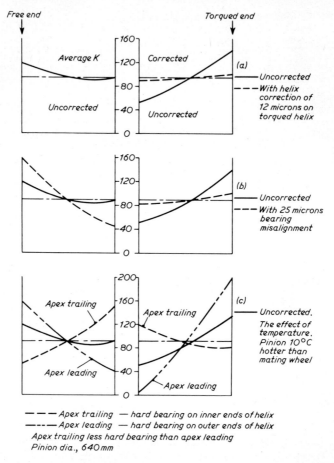

Fɪɢ. 2.5.—Effect on load distribution of helix correction, misalignment and temperature
difference. (Kerpestein).

In high speed pinions, additional heat flows into the pinion from the bearings
causing the outer ends to expand more than the inner, making the contact hard
on the outer ends. Compensation would again be obtained with apex trailing.

Hᴇʟɪx Cᴏʀʀᴇᴄᴛɪᴏɴ

For a particular mean load, the longitudinal helix correction ideally takes the
shape of the inversion of the combined deflection, so that uniform loading is
obtained at that particular load.[19] In practice however partial corrections only are
made, so that the important dimensions, base pitch and helix angle, can still be
measured. The corrected portions are at the ends of the teeth and extend inwards
for about ½ to ⅔ of the face, blending in smoothly with the uncorrected portions.
Records of the meshing at no load in the gear case, or in the meshing frame, can

thus be obtained and compared with the meshing records under load. This is achieved by applying tool makers oil resistant marking dye to the teeth of one of the meshing units and then driving one by the other, when some of the dye is transferred. What must be observed is the hard metallic marking that is evident on the dye-covered flanks. Careful study will determine the precise areas of contact to a tolerance of the order of 0·005 mm, which can be proved by a controlled change in alignment between the two gears.

The final marking is recorded by the use of transparent adhesive tape which, after application to the areas carrying the marking dye, can be peeled away with the contact pattern on the adhesive side of the tape. When fixed with the adhesive side to stiff paper, a clear and permanent record of the tooth contact is formed.[13]

MISALIGNMENT

The effects of misalignment can be visualised by including the base of the deflection diagram to decrease or increase the peak values, as occurs with favourable or adverse misalignment. Fig. 2.5b gives the calculated load distribution with a 25 μm bearing misalignment.

SPUR AND HELICAL GEARS

The bending and twisting of the pinion body will be the same whether the teeth are spur or helical and the longitudinal corrections will be correct for one particular load. Similarly, the profile corrections for spur teeth will be correct for one load giving smooth transition between the one and two pairs of teeth carrying the load. This restriction does not apply to helical gears which have an integral number of axial pitches. The total length of the line of contact with or without tip relief remains constant during the meshing cycle. There is a slight pressure concentration at the ends of the contact lines due to the buttressing effect of the adjacent unloaded portions of the teeth. This is relieved by a slight tip relief. Thus helical gears can have a smaller transmission error than spur gears, and in practice supersede spur gears for high speed and high duty gears.

3. MATERIAL COMBINATIONS AND RESULTS OF FULL-SCALE TESTING AND EXPERIENCE

Up to 1945, the majority of marine gears made in the U.K. were of oil hardened $3 \cdot 5\%$ Ni steel and $0 \cdot 4\%$ C steel, 40–50 ton/in² and 30–40 ton/in² UTS for pinions and wheel rims respectively. These relatively soft steels, at best suffered only initial pitting and were self-adjusting by wear. The tooth loading however was about 60–80K for merchant gears and up to 120K for high speed naval gears with F/d ratios of over $2 \cdot 5$.

Back-to-back gear testing carried out in the U.K., reported by Newman [38], on steam gun boat gears with these materials showed that initial pitting started at the maximum load corresponding to a K of 116. With helix correction for 200% load, pitting started at about 230K thus proving the great value of helix correction especially with large F/d ratios.

The gears were double-helical, with a face-width to diameter, F/d of $2 \cdot 58$. Further full-scale testing cn double-helical gears, with an F/d ratio of $0 \cdot 56$ with various combination of alloy steels, led to worthwhile increases in loading on EN25/EN8 and EN26/EN9, but the hardest materials capable of being hobbed and shaved were disappointing, especially the combination EN26/EN30. Although they gave tooth breakage results slightly higher than those obtained with $3 \cdot 5\%$ Ni/$0 \cdot 4\%$ C combination, they were not so good on pitting and scuffing and have shown themselves to be more sensitive to inaccuracies of mounting, profile and surface finish.

This has been borne out in service on the *Nestor* and *Neleus* ships for Alfred Holt and Co., where both pinion and wheel were made of alloy steels EN28/EN28, through-hardened to 300–330 BHN and 260–290 BHN respectively. The first reduction gears have operated without any surface deterioration but, as fully described by Darlington,[24] the second reduction gears suffered substantial dedendum wear during the early voyages, thereafter the wear stabilised and these original gears were still in service after 25 years.

This type of wear was common in the earlier days with 3% Ni pinion and $0 \cdot 4\%$ C steel wheels.[23, 25] The teeth are no longer involute. The two worn dedenda conform to the corresponding unworn addenda giving a larger bearing area than the original Hertzian flat and thereafter perform quietly and perfectly. Magnetic strainers are of course essential in the lubricating oil system.

A complete solution to the problem of the *Nestor* and *Neleus* type wear was found by adopting carburised, hardened and ground pinions mating with the same design of through-hardened alloy steel wheel. This has given excellent service.

18

Investigation [43, 45] has shown that there is an increase in surface loading of the through-hardened alloy steel wheel, when running with the surface-hardened mating pinion, beyond that when running with a through-hardened pinion. The surface finish of the surface-hardened pinion must be of high quality, about 10–20 μ-inch, as it is on that surface that the teeth of the through-hardened wheel polish and work-harden.

Case-hardened pinions on through-hardened wheels have been used successfully by the Royal Navy at 270K, in similar cases where replacement was necessary because of severe wear when using through-hardened alloy pinions and wheels in second reduction gears at 270K.[28] It is to be noted that no wear occurred on the first reduction gears with through-hardened pinions and wheels.

MAAG [41] have used case-hardened pinions on through-hardened wheels greater than 5 ft diameter for a very long time. This successful practice is well established and has a safety margin greater than that with through-hardened pinions and wheels. This has been reflected in Lloyds Rules,[49] giving an increase in surface loading of 25% for $\sigma_u = 45$ tons/in^2 (70 kg.f/mm^2) EN8 and EN9 and 18% for $\sigma_u = 85$ tons/in^2 (135 kg.f/mm^2) EN.30B.

To achieve further advances in loading, giving improved power/weight ratio and to retain the same or improved reliability, surface hardened pinions and wheels become necessary.

Investigations by the Royal Navy and Vickers Gear Research Association (NAVGRA), on full scale back-to-back gear test rigs representing first and second reduction naval gear have been reported [38, 39, 40] and service experience by Weaving and Sampson.[27]

With carburised case-hardened and ground EN36 single-helical pinions and wheels with an F/d ratio of 1·0, the loading with a dp of 2·0 reached maximum tangential loads of 15 200 lb per inch face-width, corresponding to a K value of 1350 and a specific loading $\dfrac{W_{if}}{P_n}$ of 9500 lb/in per inch pitch.

Scuffing occurred in earlier tests with a straight mineral oil OM100 but did not occur with EP oils. In general there is an optimum tooth form. With excessively large pitches there is a possibility of scuffing and with small pitches the gears fail by tooth breakage.

The excessive grinding required with carburised wheels led to an investigation of alternative surface hardening processes, viz, induction hardening and nitriding, both of which involve far less distortion.

The sensitive technique required by tooth-by-tooth induction hardening was successful in some cases. In spite of the discontinuities and variable hardness inherent in the process, loads approaching those for carburised gears were withstood on large wheels. A considerable amount of grinding was still required.

The attractions of nitriding, with its prospect of negligible distortion, and elimination of the grinding process led to tests on nitrided pinions and wheels. These have shown consistent results comparable with the best of the other two methods of hardening in spite of the much smaller case depth. The choice of material was 3% Cr.Mo nitriding steel to EN40c. With a surface hardness of about 770–800 VHN and a core strength of about 65 tons/in.^{2} The case depth was about 25–30 $\times$ 10^{-3} in, with a reasonable maximum nitriding time.

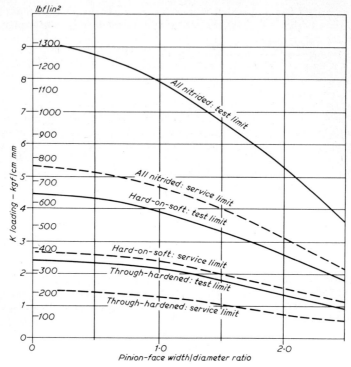

F<small>IG</small>. 3.1.—Allowable loading with various material combinations. (G.E.C.(U.K.)).

The loading with a dp of 2 reaches a maximum of 14 000 lb per inch face-width corresponding to a K value of 1250 and a specific loading $\dfrac{W_{if}}{P_n}$ of 8900 lb/in per inch pitch. These results will be discussed later in Chapter 22.

Fig. 3.1 gives an interpretation of loading possibilities on the base of pinion face-width to diameter ratio for the three alternatives: case-hardened, hard-on-soft, and through-hardened material combinations. The various Classification Societies' Rules vary on these loadings according to their experience.

Furnaces are available to nitride wheels of 120 inch diameter in the U.K. and 140 inch in Switzerland, and MAAG HSS 360 gear grinding machines are available to " lick-grind " the nitrided wheels should that be required.

Large main wheels are normally fabricated using two or more side plates connecting the rim to the hub. It has been found that because the tangential stiffness of reasonable side plates is much greater than the torsional stiffness of the hub, most of the driving torque is transmitted through the side plate nearest to the output flange.[143] Use is made of this fact in the new " Transflex wheel design ", shown in Fig. 7.5.

It is most economical to use a rim material which has good tooth bearing properties and can be welded. A range of such steels is available including nitriding steels.

4. TOOTH LOADING. USEFUL CRITERIA. RELIABILITY

The method of reducing the ultimate loads to safe practical values is given in the I.S.O. gear rating proposals for involute gears. Factors are included for influences shown to be important from laboratory and full scale tests, and experience in service.[49, b]

The ultimate limit of gear loading divided by the nominal loading is an inadequate measure of the " factor of safety ". The " margin of safety " between the distribution of the loads and strength is the determining factor in reliability, and is graphically shown in Fig. 4.1.[48, 51] Techniques are being evolved to improve the reliability of components and systems and their coupling· so that the reliability of each is not impaired.

For rough loading from external influences, the reliability of the complete gear will simply be the reliability of the weakest link in the chain i.e. tooth breakage and this is most probably caused by excessive misalignment and stiff coupling between the various systems as described later. An example where suitable coupling of the various systems was required, plus an increase in safety margins is that given by T. P. Jones.[34, 52]

To build up experience on service loads, measurements are taken regularly, on the hulls of new types of tankers and container ships, with strain recorders giving the number of times and sequences, various loads are exceeded[54] including the " once in 20 years load ". This gives the history of the " scrambled " loading used in fatigue testing. This method was first evolved by Pugsley[53] to determine an experimental statistical background for repeated loads on aircraft structures.

Similarly stresses are monitored on gear teeth in service in special cases.[62, 63]

One would suggest continuous recording of the attitude positions (Fig. 19.1) of the fore and aft main wheel journals in order to determine the load differentials on the main wheel bearings (Bunyan) so that adjustment could be made if necessary after the occasions of excessive external conditions. Monitoring is a necessary feature on large turbo-generator sets and for this purpose turbovisory gear is used.

For the purpose of this review, it is not necessary to deal with the I.S.O. rules in detail, but to come to the final rules which gives a Lloyd's K value for surface loading and a specific bending stress $\dfrac{W_{if,}^{[46, 47]}}{P_n}$ both suitably factored for all significant internal and external influences, according to the I.S.O. rules and experience.[49] These can be expressed as

22

$$K = \frac{W_{if}(r+1)}{d \quad r} \text{ and } \frac{W_{if}}{P_n} \text{ respectively where:}$$

W_{if} = the tangential load per inch face width
d = diameter of the pinion
r = the gear ratio
P_n = the normal pitch

The two expressions are of course related as follows:

$$\frac{W_{if}}{P_n} = \frac{K.d.r.}{P_n(r+1)}$$

Both expressions are useful for comparative design and appraisal.

A simplified expression for bending stress can be obtained from the MAAG Gear Book, page 121, which for a fair range of variables gives:

$$\sigma_f = \frac{W_{if}}{P_n} \times 4 \cdot 3 \text{ lb/in.}^2$$

$$\text{For internal gears: } K = \frac{W_{if}(r-1)}{d \quad r}$$

No rules are given for scuffing in the I.S.O. proposals, as experience shows this trouble to be disappearing (Toms). Nevertheless, it is usual to calculate the oil film thickness (equation 1, Chapter 20, p. 142) and the flash temperature (equation 2, Chapter 21, p. 146) for comparison with the surface finish to indicate the safety or otherwise of the gear lubrication and tooth design (see page 139). This deals with the normal running condition.[48] However, there is the possibility of asperity contact with a crash stop from full speed if there is a pause at zero rev/min. The oil film thickness is greatly reduced while the load may be 200% of the normal maximum if the astern turbine drives the L.P. train. Also the bulk temperature of the gears will be slightly less than that occurring at high speed. Under these conditions the asperities will either smooth down or tear, creating a rougher finish which may lead to scuffing at speed.

Experience with carburised, case-hardened and ground gears and nitrided gears is now extensive in both naval and industrial applications, especially with epicyclic gears. The first set of carburised, case-hardened and ground gears for the Royal Navy was designed and manufactured by MAAG in Switzerland.[28] They were single-helical and were fitted in HMS *Diana*, a Mk III Daring class destroyer (Fig. 4.2). These are still in operation at about 260K with another navy. The enormous increase in load carrying capacity and reliability of surface hardened gears is now recognised in merchant gearing.

The first high gear loading used in naval service known to the author was in the Bold Class Boats in 1946 designed and built by G.E.C.(U.K.) (Ref. 28 discussion). These were powered by G2 gas turbines at 4800 shp each at 5200 rev/min, with diesel cruising. At this service rating the gears were loaded to 580K. The gears were single-helical, carburised, case-hardened and ground, and gave no trouble.

The Y102A gearing for the County and Tribal Class Vessels, Fig. 4.3,[26] with COSAG machinery designed and manufactured by A.E.I.(G.E.C.) was carburised,

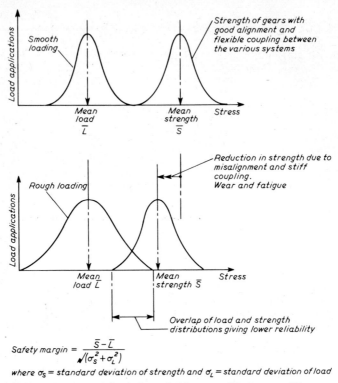

$$\text{Safety margin} = \frac{\bar{S} - \bar{L}}{\sqrt{(\sigma_S^2 + \sigma_L^2)}}$$

where σ_S = standard deviation of strength and σ_L = standard deviation of load

Note:– Standard deviation is the root of the mean of the squares of the difference from the arithmetical mean of the loads and strengths

FIG. 4.1.—Distribution of loads and strengths and their influence on reliability. (Carter, I.Mech.E. 1974.)

case-hardened and ground throughout. The maximum tooth loading was 464K on the L.P. steam second reduction and 640K on the gas astern pinion. On trials, 819K was attained on this pinion for exploratory purposes only. The gears were single-helical with a main wheel of 72-inch diameter. Later nitrided and induction hardened primary gears were also used in these vessels.

In the Finnish Navy, the Turunman class of gunboats with CODAG machinery, the Olympus engine with Brown Boveri turbine drove a single-reduction wheel of 68-inch diameter with a ratio of 12·5. Following normal Brown Boveri practice, the gears are surface hardened by nitriding and are ground in this instance, enabling gear ratings in excess of 400K to be used.[31] The gears being single-helical with thrust collars is a characteristic of Brown Boveri [32] designs (Fig. 5.1). Nitrided wheels of 96-inch diameter by Brown Boveri are in naval service. The maximum size at present is 140-inch diameter, determined by the grinding machine and nitriding furnace capacity.

In merchant gearing built since 1950, the combination EN25/EN8 has given excellent service at 85K and 75K in the first and second reduction.[38] Alloy steels of

Gear	Normal pitch, in	K factor, max.	S_b, ton/in^2	Material, per cent	Manufacture, single helical
Primary pinion	0·7947 h.p.	263	3·56	3 NiCr	Carburized-hardened and ground
Primary wheel	0·8185 l.p.		3·64		
Secondary pinion	1·154	200	3·63	4½ NiCr	Air hardened
Main wheel			2·82		

Fig. 4.2.—MAAG design ' Daring ' Mk. 111 for HMS *Diana*. (Gowans and Porter, I.Mech.E. 1970).

Ni.Cr.Mo. allow greater loading and are used at 140K and 110K. These require special care, as does all gearing, but their possible troubles are overcome by using " hard on soft " combinations, as previously mentioned, and are running at 160K and 130K for primary and secondary gears.[36]

Nitrided gears have great potential and are used in merchant service at 280K in all but the final reduction gear.

Carburised, case-hardened and ground gears can be used at the highest loading. Different Classification Society Rules vary from 270K to 340K for first reductions.

Fig. 4.3.—Section view of Y102 gearbox Port Set. (G.E.C.(U.K.)).

Large carburised, case-hardened and ground gears are not feasible and current practice is to use " hard on soft ", as already mentioned.

The difference in loading between naval and merchant gears is seen to be quite large and, while the latter is conservative, it must be remembered that combat naval vessels operate for a small fraction of their life at and near full load, but have severe reversing requirements, whereas tankers and container ships operate for most of their 20 year life at and about full load.

Surface hardening is used with double-helical as well as with single-helical gears.

5. FEATURES OF SINGLE-
AND DOUBLE-HELICAL GEARS

Several points about single- and double-helical surface hardened gears are noted:

Single-helical

Comparative simplicity in grinding. No gap. Low helix angle—15°.

Complete absence of pinion shuttling, obviating the use of sliding couplings.

Axial thrust on primary high speed pinion unless taken by turbine thrust bearing can lead to high losses if flooded thrust pads are used.

Thrust cones are used by Brown Boveri [32] to overcome this (Fig. 5.1).

Ball and roller bearings have been used with marinised aero-engines with low loss.

Quill shafts can be solidly coupled to primary wheels and secondary pinion, the helix angle on each being arranged to balance the axial thrusts.

A simple side bearing serves to locate the shafts. The axial thrust of the

Double-helical

Longer grinding times. Normal gap with MAAG 0° grinding method. Normal helix angles—30°.

Apex wander due to different composite pitch errors causing shuttling. Gear tooth couplings do not respond because of the high frictional loads. Best compromise is to use axially flexible couplings. With highly accurate gears this effect is small.

No axial thrust and no high speed thrust bearings required. Final reduction wheel located by propeller thrust bearing.

final reduction wheel is carried by the propeller thrust bearing.

Experience shows that the effect of the axial tilting moment on wheels is not noticeable when the product of the gear diameter, face-width and tangent of the helix angle ÷ (bearing span)² $\leqq$ 0·16 to 0·22 [41]

i.e. $\dfrac{d\,F \tan \sigma}{L^2} \leqq 0{\cdot}16$ to $0{\cdot}22$.

No tilting moments.

Small helix errors can be perfectly corrected by adjusting the pinion bearings.

Helix errors can also be corrected by adjusting the bearings but not so perfectly as with single helical gears.

The main advantage of the double-helical gear is that it does not develop axial thrust. The gears, however, take more time in manufacture and are slightly heavier.

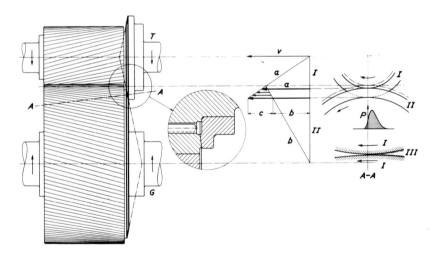

FIG. 5.1.—Brown Boveri thrust collar to absorb the axial thrust of single-helical gear wheels.

I	= Pinion	P	= Pressure in oil film
II	= Wheel	v	= Speed
III	= Oil	a	= Peripheral speed of pinion
G	= Driven	b	= Peripheral speed of wheel
T	= Driving	c	= Sliding speed at collar.

THRUST CONES

With the Brown Boveri cone system there is line contact and a very large relative radius of curvature with a large oil entraining velocity, giving a minimum oil

Fɪɢ. 5.2.—A single helical three lay shaft gear with thrust cones by David Brown Industries
for A.E.I. Limited.
2500 kW – 10 000/1500 rpm.

film thickness of the order of 0·005 in for an 8 in diameter pinion with a peripheral velocity of 220 ft/s. There is thus considerable axial resilience.

With the large radius of curvature, a small radial width on the cone is sufficient
to take the thrust which, in the example stated, would be of the order of 9000 lb
at a 1000K on the pinion teeth.

Fig. 5.2 shows their use in a single-helical, three layshaft reduction gear built
by David Brown Industries.

6. EXTERNAL INFLUENCES

The gearcase and mounting systems must ensure that the gears remain aligned when under the input and output torques, the gearcase taking the reaction torque. This is achieved with modern gearboxes whether they are of the rigid combined box type or have separate boxes for each set of gears in the same transverse plane.

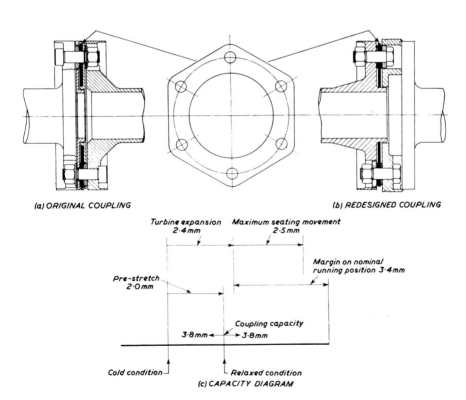

Fig. 6.1.—Turbine flexible coupling and cold setting positions for turbine and gear. (G.E.C.(U.K.)). IMAS 73/pp.1/43).

31

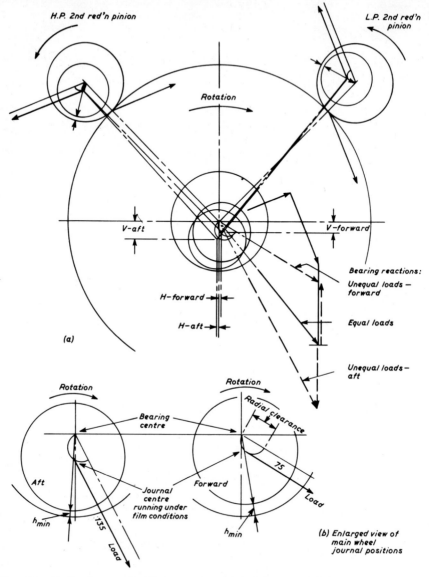

H.P. 2nd red'n pinion

L.P. 2nd red'n pinion

Rotation

V-aft

V-forward

Bearing reactions:

Unequal loads —
forward

Equal loads

Unequal loads—
aft

H-forward

H-aft

(a)

Rotation

Rotation

Radial clearance

Bearing
centre

75

Aft

Forward

Load

Journal
centre
running under
film conditions

135

h_{min}

h_{min}

Load

(b) Enlarged view of
main wheel
journal positions

FIG. 6.2.—(a) Bearing reaction diagram and position of fore and after journal positions with unequal loads due to external couple from line shaft. Shaft running under film conditions. (b) Enlarged view of main wheel journal positions.

Relative positions:

HP pinion and main wheel		LP pinion and main wheel	
(i) unequal centres	— slight	(i) unequal centres	— aft end out of mesh
(ii) out of plane of journals	— hard on aft end of mesh	(ii) out of plane	— slight.

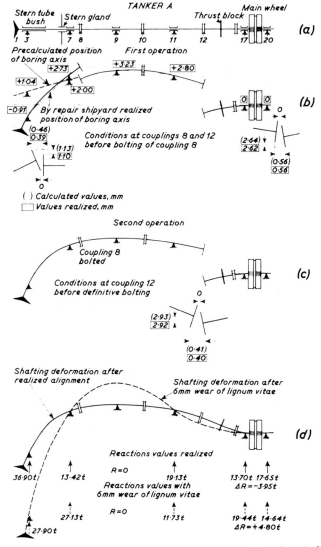

FIG. 6.3.—Practical realisation of rational alignment of propulsive plant shafting.
(IMAS 1969, pp. 15/26—Volcy).

Under pure torque the journals of the pinion and wheels adjust themselves according to the loading and hydrodynamic action in the clearance bearings, bending and twisting of the pinion being catered for by helix correction.

At the input, misalignment with the input turbine takes place due to thermal expansion and possibly other changes. With correct cold setting of the turbine relative to the pinion, the flexible couplings and quill shaft can take care of the changes in alignment under operating conditions (see Fig. 6.1).[36]

The alignment is much more critical at the main wheel-line shaft connection and has a very great influence on the reliability of the gearing. The double-bottom structure on which the machinery is seated deflects with changes in the loading of the ship, sea conditions, tilting of thrust block on the line shaft and temperature effects. These influences can change the loading and give rise to a bending moment at the main wheel aft coupling flange, resulting in a cocking of the wheel in the clearance bearings, so misaligning the rim of the main wheel relative to the secondary pinions (Figs. 6.2a and 2b).[55, 56, 57]

In smaller vessels, with engines placed amidships, the line shafting is quite flexible and the line shaft bearings can be so arranged that their displacement can have negligible effect on the main wheel bearing loads.

Fig. 6.3a from Volcy[56] shows a typical main wheel-line shaft-propeller arrangement for a tanker with the engine placed well aft. The small span of the main wheel bearings will be observed. It will be appreciated that even small movements, particularly of the forward supporting line shaft bearing No. 4, can result in large

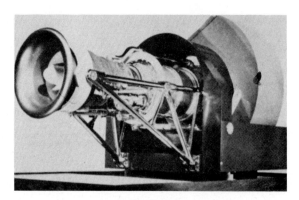

Fig. 6.4.—Olympus mounting arrangement.

changes in the main wheel bearing loads; therefore this bearing should be as far removed from the gear-box as possible.

It is best to use as few bearings in the line shafting as possible consistent with specific loading on the bearings and whirling considerations. This ensures flexibility and reduces the effects of hull distortion and bearing wear-down.

Briefly the analysis of the line shafting gives the bearing loads, bending moments, shaft deflections and influence numbers by treating the shaft as a continuous beam, straight aligned. The influence numbers indicate the change in each bearing load, per unit deflection in any one bearing. From this, the bearings are raised or lowered by additional amounts, to allow for hull deflections and movements of the gearcase due to thermal expansion, to give near equal loads on the fore and aft main wheel bearings and positive loads on all other supports. On uncoupling the flanges, there is a " gap and sag " at each flange, the values of which are required during assembly. The final check can be made on bearing loads by using hydraulic jacks and strain gauges.

The excellent example given by Volcy[56] in Fig. 6.3b shows the first operation with the shaft bearings placed at precalculated positions and the uncoupled shafts with their " gap and sag ".

Fig. 6.3c shows the second operation with the propeller shaft coupled and the final " gap and sag ". Calculated and measured values are also given.

Fig. 6.3d shows the final shaft deformation after complete alignment with each bearing correctly loaded. The dotted line shows the shafting deformation after 6 mm wear of the lignum vitae in the stern tube bush. Reasonable loading has been achieved on the fore and aft bearings of the main wheel. As all bearings have downward loading the shaft whirling speeds will be as calculated and outside the running range.

These investigations also showed the deleterious effect of having journal bearings within the thrust bearing housing, creating bending moments in the thrust shaft. The thrust pads should be thrust balanced and pivoted to enable the bearing to accommodate alignment disturbances, and the housing should be supported on the plane, in line with the centre-line of the shaft, that is " centre-line mounted ".

Calculated and measured values of " gap and sag " include the calculations of the deformation of the engine room seating. Such structural calculations are made possible by three-dimensional finite element analysis. This method interconnects the bending moments, shear force, deflections and rotations of small discrete components which may be beams, plates or shells and finally gives the internal forces and deflections of the structure.

This powerful method is used to design the double-bottom structure, gearcase seating, the centre-line thrust block and shaft bearing supports. With the larger ships a great amount of steel is necessary to obtain acceptable deflections under propeller-excited forces and sea conditions and it is due in part to these intensive analyses that gearing is successful in present-day ships.

It is recognised, however, that with larger and more flexible ships with larger powers at lower rev/min, giving shorter and stiffer shafts, there is a technical limit to the stiffening which can be built into the aft end of the ships and thus the alignment of the main wheel becomes more vulnerable. A step-advance must be made.

In support of this, attention is drawn to the marinised aero-engine, the gas-generator of which is " repaired by quick replacement " and is flexibly mounted similar to that in an aircraft, and is therefore free from external influences (Fig. 6.4), whereas the main wheel, which is the basic anchor component and which, like the rest of the gears, must last the life of the ship without removal, is left traditionally at the mercy of the sea conditions on a relatively flexible hull.

A new philosophy to overcome these troubles has been applied by Bunyan,[59] Fig. 6.5.

The wheel is supported and located axially by its own journals on two outer plates welded to the rim and a single plate diaphragm, welded to the centre of the rim and the hub, drives the main wheel shaft. Thus this " Transflex wheel " provides angular and axial flexibility at the ideal position leaving the output shaft

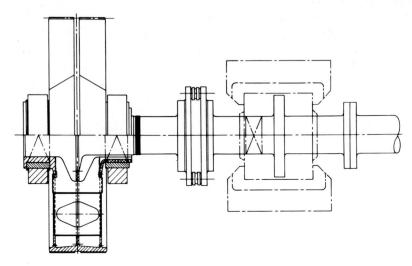

Fig. 6.5.—Transflex wheel with flexible coupling giving the Cardan shaft effect. (Bunyan).

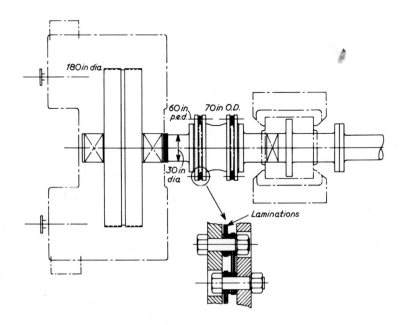

Fig. 6.6.—Main shaft flexible coupling. (I.Mar.E. IMAS 73. I. T. Young).

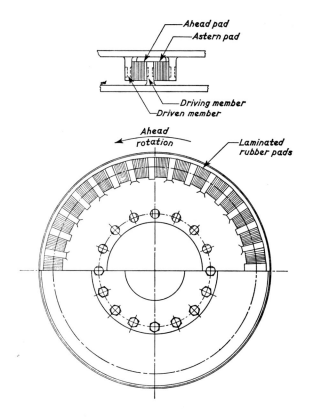

Fig. 6.7.—Vickers high-torque capacity flexible coupling. (Verity).

independent of the bearing journals. A disc type flexible coupling, fitted aft of the thrust block, could be used with the " Transflex " wheel to give the desired " Cardan " shaft effect. An alternative proposal for the very large ship is the use of flexible couplings fitted between the main wheel and the thrust block. Fig. 6.6 shows a turboflex type by I. T. Young [60] and Fig. 6.7 shows the Vickers [61] high torque capacity coupling which drives through laminated rubber pads.

Both types are perfectly practicable and have been designed for the purpose of maintaining substantially equal loads on the fore and aft main wheel bearings.

These proposals would appear to be going beyond the " state of the art ", but the problems of the bigger ships are forcing the development, and designers must be ready with practical solutions.

An alternative method which has been used for some time is to support a combined gearcase, of the rigid type, on a flexible three-point support. Two spherically-shaped trunnions, of the flexing type, are fitted athwart the main wheel

FIG. 6.8.—Turbine-Condenser-Gear Power Package, all bolted together to form a rigid
self-supporting structure. (MAAG 69).

while the third is on the centre line and is purposely made less rigid, so that it
allows free movement and does not control the attitude of the gearcase.[58]

Similar systems have been used in naval plant, where the reduction gear condenser and turbines are bolted together, giving a rigid self-supporting structure.
Again, two spherically-shaped supports are mounted athwartships under the
centre line of the gear, and the third point, a sliding member, is situated on the
axial centre line at the forward end of the condenser. This method has also been
used by Brown Boveri and MAAG. Figs. 6.8 and 6.9 show such an arrangement
by MAAG.[41]

FIG. 6.9.—View from below of Power Package showing the three point flexible support. (MAAG 69).

7. GEARING CONFIGURATIONS

About 1960 there was a rapid increase in the size of tankers and bulk carriers, and corresponding increases in power with larger, slower-running propellers, 80–90 rev/min giving a higher propulsive efficiency. At the same time, the high speed container ship was introduced, with relatively high powers and a propeller speed of about 120 rev/min, determined by the limited draught.

Headroom and the space available were determining factors in the configuration of the whole installation, the traditional three-plane, single-tandem, articulated gear arrangement, with through-hardened gears being too high and bulky (Figs. 7.1, 2, 3 and 4).

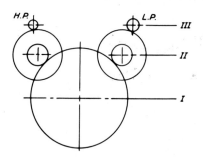

Fig. 7.1.—Three-plane group.

This led to the single-plane arrangement introduced by G.E.(U.S.A.) and Stal Laval. Every unit was reduced to one level, including the condenser which was arranged forward of the L.P. turbine, thus giving a low engine room (Fig. 7.5).

Figs. 7.6a and b show the Stal Laval A.P. single-plane arrangement for powers above 10 MW. The novel feature is the adoption of epicyclic gears for the primary reduction, the planet carrier being overhung from the pinion of a conventional final reduction train. For large gear ratios, triple reduction is used. This takes the form of a star gear and planetary gear on the H.P. line. The star gear is located at the forward end of the pinion and its casing, to which the planet carrier is attached, is integral with the H.P. turbine bedplate.

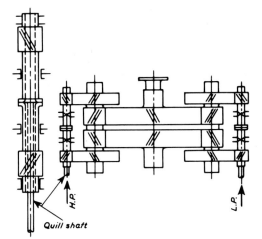

FIG. 7.2.—Split primary gear train.

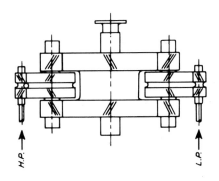

FIG. 7.3.—Split secondary gear train.

FIG. 7.4.—Double reduction three-plane group tandem articulated.

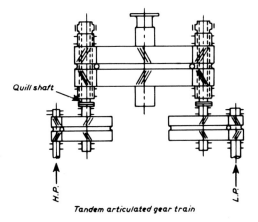

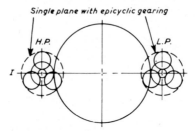

FIG. 7.5.—Single plane with epicyclic gearing.

The final reduction is a double-helical parallel shaft gear with pinions and wheel rim of through-hardened material. The final reduction gearcase is a symmetrical single-walled box, supported at four points, two athwartships in line with main wheel diameter and and two fore and aft on the centre line. Complementary with the supports are two pairs of adjustable spring packs which provide self-adjustment to the shafting misalignment and hull movements, thereby protecting the gear mesh. The secondary pinions are free to slide axially because of the· axial freedom of the planets on their bearing oil film. This is an excellent feature.

To date there are over 1000 planetary trains at sea with an availability of 99·6%.

Two-plane arrangements have been used by De Schelde, A.E.G., G.E.C.(U.K.) and Westinghouse, thus accommodating the traditional underslung condenser by having the turbines on a higher plane (Figs. 7.7a and b). The headroom is similar to that with the single plane, because the determining factor is the height necessary to lift the main wheel from its casing. Kemper (De Schelde) [65] shows an alternative proposal for the two-plane arrangement, where large reduction ratios are required from the H.P. turbine at 7200 rev/min to 80 rev/min at the propeller. The primary reduction could be a Renk compound star gear, giving up to 17 : 1 reduction ratio, overhung from the final reduction pinion (Fig. 7.8). In the star gear, the planet wheel carrier is stationary and is more suitable for reduction from high speed than the planetary gear, as the centrifugal forces on the planets do not arise. The annulus is supported by Renk " sleeve " spring packs, the flexibility of which can be adjusted to give the required torsional characteristics. The springs also give some bending flexibility and damping. This resilience and axial freedom from the secondary pinions gives greater isolation to the gear.

All these developments have only one second reduction pinion per input, thus the full economic potential of the main wheel is not utilised. For higher powers, with relatively low propeller shaft rev/min, the locked-train type of gear is universally adopted (Figs. 7.9 7.10a and b). Locked-train gearing is arranged either in a combined box, containing all the rotating elements, or in separate boxes, each containing a set of meshing gears. The aim in both types is to ensure equal deflections of the bearing supports of each gear, relative to its mating gear under load. Helix angles are modified as necessary on the pinions, to compensate for pinion torsion and bending to ensure uniform full face contact and loading under full load conditions.

A separate box arrangement is used by Stal Laval in their locked-train higher torque applications, as shown in Figs. 7.11a and b. The two locked-train boxes are

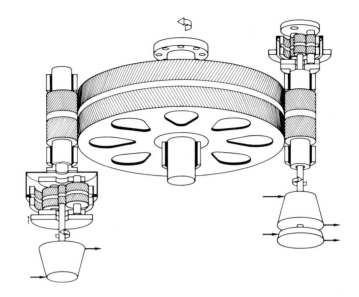

FIG. 7.6a.—Basic principles of Stal Laval A.P. single plane gearing with double reduction.

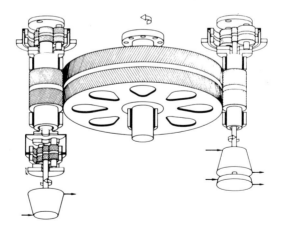

FIG. 7.6b.—Basic principles of Stal Laval A.P. single plane with triple reduction for H.P. turbine drive gearing.

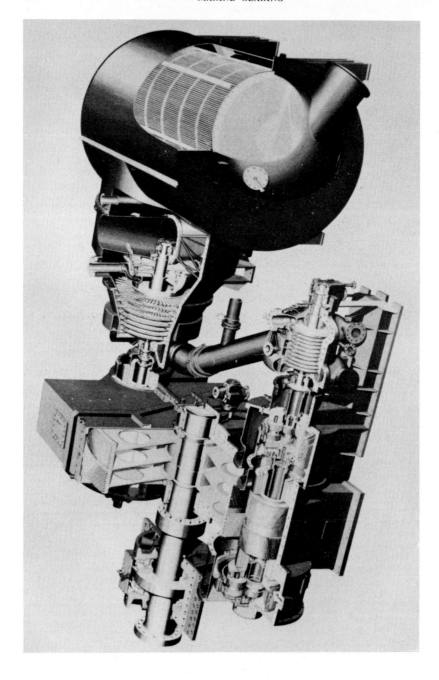

FIG. 7.6c.—Stal Laval single plane machinery for powers above 10 MW.

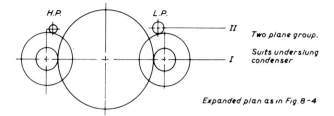

FIG. 7.7.—Two plane gearing with parallel shaft primary gears.

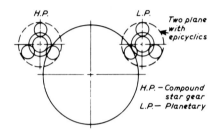

FIG. 7.8a.—Two plane gearing with epicyclic primaries.

separate from the final reduction box, which again has two main supports in the plane of the gears and another two in line with their axes. These can be adjusted to improve alignment if required. Symmetry is again the feature applying also to the locked-train boxes. Single walls are used throughout. A star gear is used in the H.P. turbine line and is bolted to the turbine bedplate. Long quill shafts provide necessary flexibility.

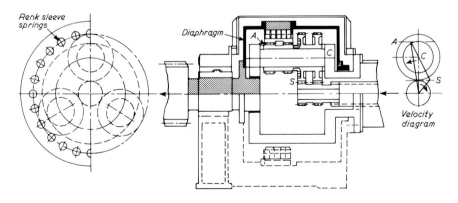

FIG. 7.8b.—Renk compound star gear. The annulus is supported by sleeve springs.

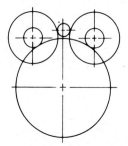

Fig. 7.9.—Single cylinder dual tandem articulated gearing (locked train).

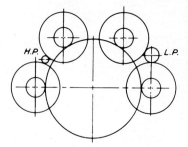

Fig. 7.10a.—Compound turbine dual tandem articulated gearing.

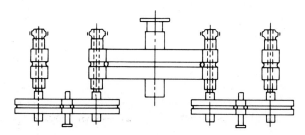

Fig. 7.10b.—Expanded plan view of compound turbine dual tandem articulated gearing as in Fig. 10a.

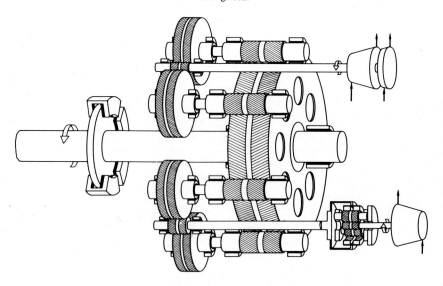

Fig. 7.11a.—Basic principle of the Stal Laval A.P. multiplane machinery for powers above 35 MW.

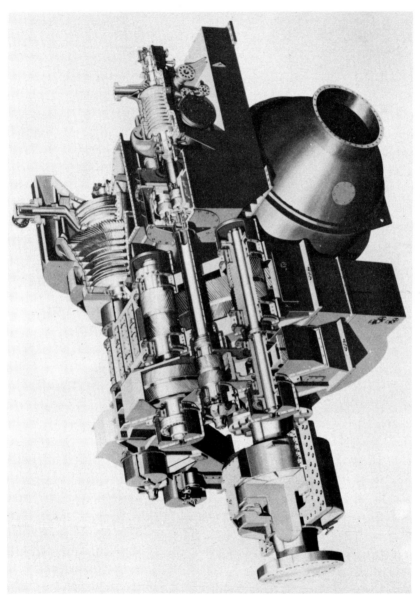

Fig. 7.11b.—Stal Laval locked-train gearing for A.P. multiplane machinery for powers above 35 MW. The primary locked train and final reduction gears are in separated gearboxes for symmetry and adjustment.

FIG. 7.12.– " Nestor " class cargo ship machinery. The primary gears are all contained in one single gearcase: the secondary gears are in a separate case.

FIG. 7.13.—Type A. tanker machinery. There are three gearcases in this equipment, two primary and one secondary.

FIG. 7.14.—Type B. tanker machinery. The dual tandem, double-reduction gearing is all mounted in a single case.

FIGS. 7.12, 7.13, and 7.14.—Gear arrangements of separate and combined gearboxes in the post 1945 era. (G.E.C.(U.K.)).

On the other hand, the combined box is more rigid and compact and can have a three-point support, again with the two main supports in the plane of the main wheel and the third in line with the final shaft axis. G.E.(U.S.A.), MAAG and G.E.(U.K.) are examples of this type and each have distinctive features. Typical arrangements of separate and combined boxes, in post-1945 gearing, are shown in Figs. 7.12, 7.13 and 7.14 (AEI).

G.E.(U.S.A.) has large numbers of the combined box type in both naval and merchant service (MST 14), with double-helical, through-hardened gears of hardness range 302–352 BHN for pinions and 223–262 BHN for the wheel rims, operating for merchant service at nominal K factors of 140/110 for the first and second reductions.

MAAG, who pioneered single-helical, hardened and ground gears, have a wide experience in both the naval and merchant field. For low head room, they have developed a range of extremely compact locked-train boxes. Fig. 7.15 shows the MAAG marine gear type 2.D.T.A.–280 being prepared on the test bed for a full-speed, no-load test.[35] It is noted that one of each of the intermediate gears of the H.P. and L.P. reductions is in the same horizontal plane as the main wheel.

This reduces the height of the gears and makes an extremely compact assembly, yet with all parts very accessible.

It will be noted that all these gearboxes have a bottom section, to take the main wheel, and a top section carrying the other rotating elements. A unique design of gearbox has been developed by G.E.C.(U.K.), in which all the bearings, including those of the main wheel, which are underslung, are bolted to a single fabricated structure, as in Fig. 7.16.

This arched structure has double walls, with closed box sections, and is extremely rigid to twisting and yet has sufficient flexibility, in the planes of the tooth forces, to ensure equal stiffness for each pair of bearing supports. Adjustable bearings enable gear alignment to be perfected at any stage of manufacture, or in service.

The main wheel housings become an integral part of the structure by " heat tightened " bolting, and form a base across the arch which materially increases the rigidity of the structure. Access to the main bearings is by removal of the bearing covers, without disturbing the housings themselves.

Lifting of the gearcase is through strength members transferring the weight from the main bearing housings direct to the lifting bosses at the top of the gearcase, as

FIG. 7.15.—MAAG Marine Gear, Type 2.D.T.A.–280. being prepared on the test bed for a full speed no-load test.
The gearing is of the single helical type, case-hardened and ground with the final reduction wheel generally through-hardened, and is contained in a single robust and compact gearcase.

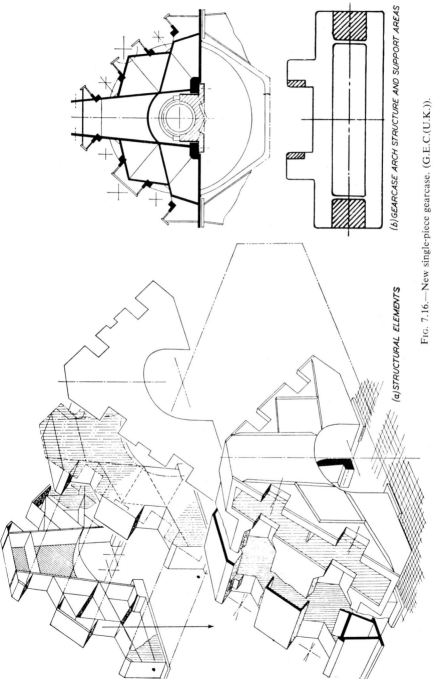

(b) GEARCASE ARCH STRUCTURE AND SUPPORT AREAS

(a) STRUCTURAL ELEMENTS

Fig. 7.16.—New single-piece gearcase. (G.E.C.(U.K.)).

Fig. 7.17.—Complete G.E.C.(U.K.) single-piece gearcase being lifted for shipment.

shown in Fig. 7.17. Figs. 7.18 and 7.19 show the G.E.C. single-piece gearbox in course of construction, assembly and in preparation for test, respectively. Support for the gearcase is on four areas, two in line with the plane of the gears and two smaller ones placed fore and aft.

Comparable gear designs, to the same load factors for 50 000 shp at 80 rev/min, for cross-compound turbines are shown in Fig. 7.20.[30]

Design A is a dual tandem parallel shaft arrangement, with case-hardened pinions and primary wheels (hard-on-hard to 300 K) and a through-hardened final reduction wheel of 165 inch diameter (hard-on-soft to 170K). Designs B and C, with final reduction epicyclic gears, show alternative approaches.

Design B uses triple-reduction with first reduction epicyclic gears, second reduction parallel shaft gearing and a final reduction epicyclic gear with a low gear ratio of about 3 : 1, permitting the use of five planet wheels with an annulus of about 110 inch diameter.

Fig. 7.18.—G.E.C.(U.K.) single-piece gearcases in course of construction.

Design C uses a first reduction parallel shaft gear and a final reduction epicyclic gear with a gear ratio of about 6 : 1 with three planet wheels. The annulus would be about 180 inch diameter with a K of 250.

Each design would be considered for particular applications.

The effect of a smaller gear ratio and an increase in the practical number of planets is to reduce the size of the annulus for a given torque factor HP/N.

For very large torques at low speed, large pitch spur teeth of 1·5 dp could be used in the above example, inspired by the experience of MAAG with large spur tooth pitches, where robust gearing is required in industrial applications.[76]

For very low speeds, e.g. 50 rev/min, G.E.C.(U.K.) has developed a double locked-train for a single-turbine drive, still using the single-piece structure, with all bearings adjustable except the main wheel bearings. Fig. 7.21 shows the arrangement for a single-input, triple-reduction gear of 20 000 shp at 50 rev/min. Dual tandem gearing is used successively, giving four final reduction pinions for the single-input drive.

This principle can be extended to eight final reduction pinions, as shown in Fig. 7.22, giving torque ratios as high as 1600 HP/N.

This would require a propeller of about 48 ft diameter and 180 tons.

The present-day manufacturing limit for solid propellers is about 90 tons and 40 ft diameter, giving a torque capacity of about 700 HP/N.[67]. The limit for built-up propellers is about 1200 HP/N. The scheme shown in Fig. 7.22 can go beyond

Fig. 7.19.—G.E.C.(U.K.) single-piece gearcases in course of assembly and in preparation for test.

this, thus making the point that suitable gearing can be built to match the maximum capacity of the propeller.

The layshaft gear shown in Fig. 7.23 would be a suitable primary gear for the L.P. turbines.

Final reduction epicyclic gearing could be "doubled-up" to give very large torque outputs, as in the Paraplan secondary gear (Fig. 8.11), which virtually has two systems in parallel.

Gearing for other propeller arrangements is available. Fig. 7.24 shows a Stal-Laval arrangement for overlapping propellers, which, from model tests, gives a higher propulsive efficiency than with single- or twin-screw. One propeller is placed aft of the other and is phased to avoid the tip vortices from the forward propeller. One H.P. and two L.P. turbines give a neat arrangement.

Fig. 7.25 shows a CODOG drive for a naval patrol boat—G.E.C.(U.K.). The gas turbine drive is basically similar to the H.P. turbine drive in Fig. 7.24. The controllable pitch propellers operate as a straightforward, twin-screw arrangement giving an exceptionally good manoeuvring performance.

Schemes for driving contra-rotating propellers are shown in Figs. 7.26 and 7.27 for parallel shaft gears giving interlocked propellers, and Figs. 7.28a and 7.28b for epicyclic gears giving torque-balanced speed conditions. With epicyclic gearing driving contra-rotating propellers, the hydrodynamic torques of the propellers automatically match the mechanical torques of the reaction members, thereby affecting the speeds and power distribution.

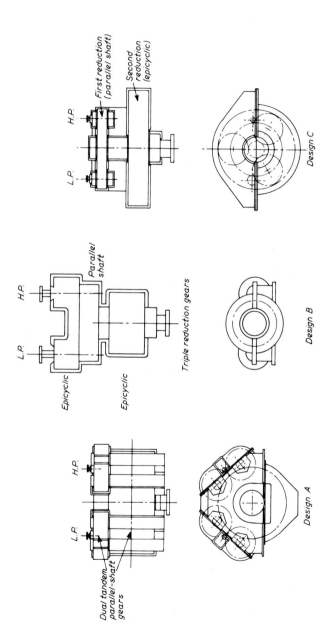

Fig. 7.20.—Comparable gear designs, to the same load factors, for 50,000 shp at 80 rev/min with cross-compound turbines. (Shannon and Young. I.Mech.E. 1970).

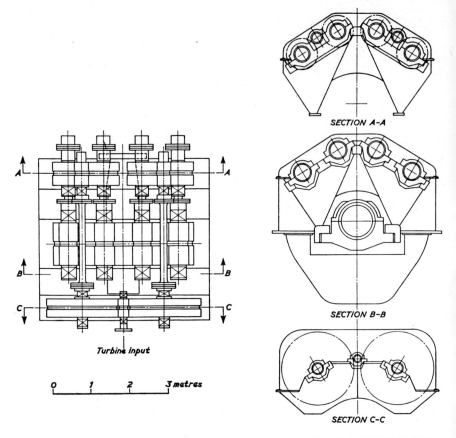

SECTION A-A

SECTION B-B

Turbine input

SECTION C-C

FIG. 7.21.—Single input triple reduction gear for 20,000 shp at 50 rev/min. (G.E.C.(U.K.)).

This can be seen by considering the final reduction epicyclic arrangement. Fig. 7.29.

(1) $\dfrac{\text{Carrier torque } Q_C}{\text{Annulus torque } Q_A} = \dfrac{A + S}{A}$

(2) $\dfrac{\text{Hydrodynamic torque from propeller on carrier}}{\text{Hydrodynamic torque from propeller on annulus}} = \dfrac{K_C D^5{}_C N^2{}_C}{K_A D^5{}_A N^2{}_A}$

where A and S are the diameters of the annulus and sun respectively, D_C and D_A are the diameters of the aft and forward propellers driven from the carrier and annulus respectively and the corresponding torque coefficients K.

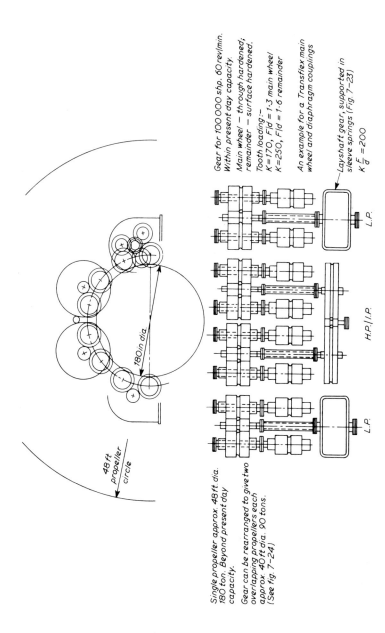

Single propeller approx. 48 ft. dia.
180 ton. Beyond present day
capacity.

Gear can be rearranged to give two
overlapping propellers each
approx. 40 ft dia. 90 tons.
(See fig. 7-24)

Gear for 100 000 shp. 60 rev/min.
Within present day capacity.

Main wheel — through hardened;
remainder — surface hardened.

Tooth loading:-
K=170, F/d = 1·3 main wheel
K=250, F/d = 1·6 remainder

An example for a Transflex main
wheel and diaphragm couplings

Layshaft gear, supported in
sleeve springs (Fig. 7-23)
$K\frac{F}{d} = 200$

L.P.

H.P./I.P.

L.P.

Fig. 7.22.—Gear for 100,000 shp 60 rev/min within present day capacity but beyond propeller
manufacturing capacity.

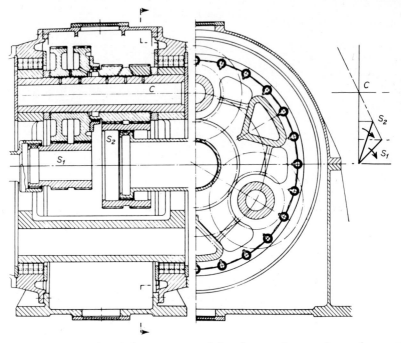

F$_{IG}$. 7.23.—Renk three lay shaft gear supported by sleeve springs, used as primary gears for the L.P. turbine drive for the arrangement shown in Fig. 7.22.

Take $\dfrac{A}{S} = 5$ and $\dfrac{D_C}{D_A} = 0\cdot9$ for the aft propeller to come within the tip vortices from the forward propeller and assume $K_c = K_A$ for a start. Then $\dfrac{Q_C}{Q_A} = 1\cdot2$;

$\dfrac{N_c}{N_A} = 1\cdot42$ from which $\dfrac{\text{carrier power}}{\text{annulus power}} = 1\cdot7.$

Such a distribution of power and speed will reduce the overall efficiency which follows from the propeller load factor

$$Bp = \frac{N.\,HP^{\frac{1}{2}}}{V_a^{\,2\cdot5}} = K^{\frac{1}{2}}_q\left(\frac{ND}{V_a}\right)^{2\cdot5}$$

A better result would be obtained with the epicyclic gears in the first reduction as shown in Fig. 7.28b, giving a choice of second reduction gear ratios and probably with the carrier driving the forward propeller.

Standard machinery schemes have been developed for naval purposes. Progress towards these from " all steam ", COSAG, and COGOG, etc. has been described by E.

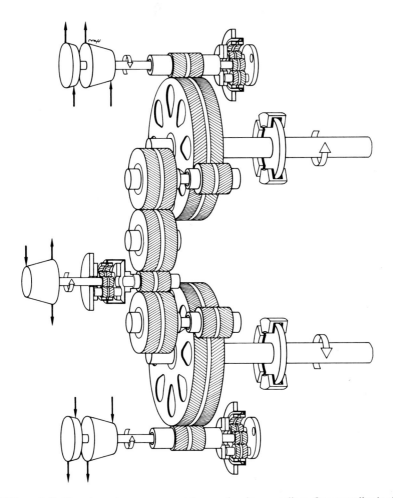

FIG. 7.24a.—A Stal-Laval gearing arrangement for overlapping propellers. One propeller is placed aft of the other and is phased to avoid the tip vortices from the forward propeller.

Norton.[64] " Recent developments in surface-warship propulsion have been based on the use of marinised aero-gas turbines arranged as COGOG (combined gas or gas), i.e. small gas turbines driving the ship at cruising powers, but larger gas turbines driving at higher powers. Other schemes are available such as COGAG, etc.

As standard components for these schemes, the Royal Navy has chosen the Rolls-Royce Olympus and the Tyne gas turbines. Their respective maximum power turbine speeds are 5600 rev/min and 13 500 rev/min."

As an example from other navies, the Canadian Armed Forces, for their DDH Class of helicopter-carrying destroyers, use Pratt and Whitney Aero FT4 and FT12

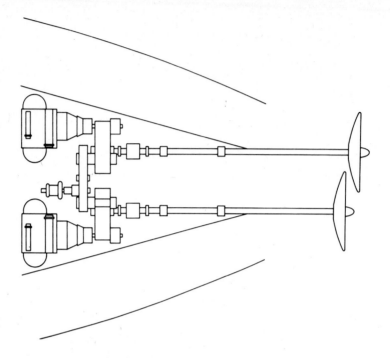

FIG. 7.24b.—Stal-Laval engine-room layout for overlapping propellers.

for boost and cruise respectively, with maximum power turbine speeds of 3600/230 rev/min and 9000/133 rev/min respectively—R. M. Sach.[166] The powers are approximately similar to those of the Rolls-Royce engines.

This example is taken to show how the gearing configuration is affected by the ship requirements and the DDH 280 is briefly described because of many other features appropriate to this review.

The DDH 280 is a twin-screw, helicopter-carrying destroyer. Each propeller is driven by one main and one cruising turbine as a COGOG arrangement. To get maximum deck space for the helicopters, the engines are placed side by side to keep the intakes and exhausts close together. This determines the disposition of the engines as shown in Fig. 7.31a. The main machinery, including all four turbines, both gear boxes and gas turbines, is put on a raft (Fig. 7.30), which floats on rubber vibration-attenuating mounts which are attached to the hull structure.

A Vulcan coupling (Fig. 7.31a) of torque capacity HP/N = 100 is used on the gearbox output drive to the propeller shaft and combines with the flexibility of the light shafting.

The gearing is single-helical designed and manufactured by MAAG Gear Wheel Co., Zurich. All gears and pinions are hardened and ground. The hardening process is by carburising except the main wheel and the FT.12 primary wheel, both of which are nitrided.

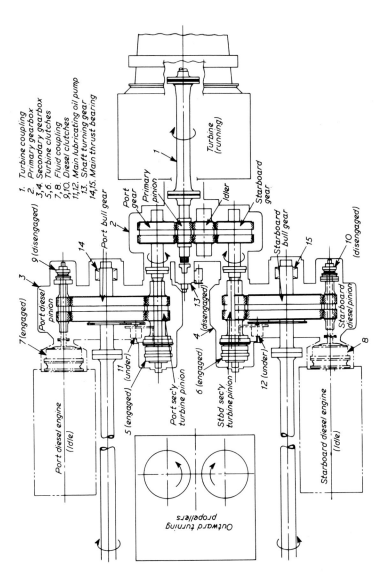

1. Turbine coupling
2. Primary gearbox
3,4. Secondary gearbox
5,6. Turbine clutches
7,8. Fluid coupling
9,10. Diesel clutches
11,12. Main lubricating oil pump
13. Shaft turning gear
14,15. Main thrust bearing

FIG. 7.25.—CODOG drive for Naval patrol boats. (G.E.C.(U.K.)). The propellers operate as a twin-screw arrangement.

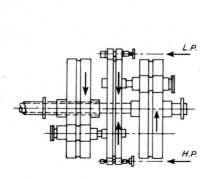

FIG. 7.26.—Parallel shaft gearing
for contra-rotating interlocked
propellers. (Michel, A.E.G.).

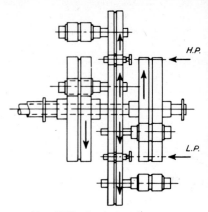

FIG. 7.27.—Locked train system
for contra-rotating interlocked
propellers. (G.E.C.(U.K.)).

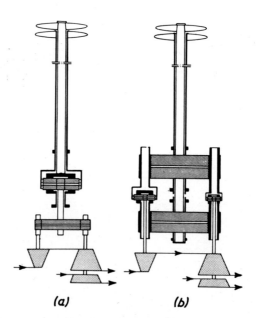

(a)   (b)

FIG. 7.28.—a and b. Contra-rotating propellers with epicyclic gearing. (Jung—Stal-Laval).

Thrust collars are fitted on the secondary pinions to eliminate thrust bearings
at the intermediate shaft—gear I/pinions II—and to reduce the tilting effect on
the second reduction gear. Because of the flexible coupling between the gears
and the main thrust block, there is a small thrust bearing at the gear output shaft
taking care of the axial load transmitted by the flexible coupling.

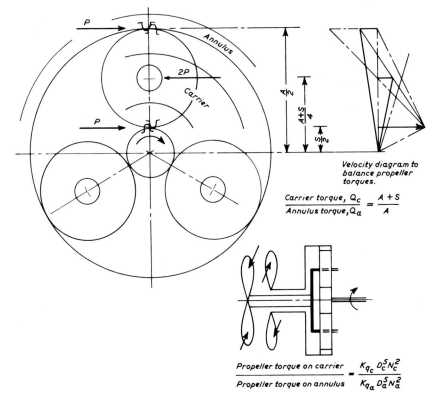

Velocity diagram to balance propeller torques.

$$\frac{\text{Carrier torque, } Q_c}{\text{Annulus torque, } Q_a} = \frac{A+S}{A}$$

$$\frac{\text{Propeller torque on carrier}}{\text{Propeller torque on annulus}} = \frac{K_{q_c} D_c^5 N_c^2}{K_{q_a} D_a^5 N_a^2}$$

FIG. 7.29.—Contra-rotating propellers driven by epicyclic gears. The hydrodynamic torques of the propellers automatically match the mechanical torques of the reaction members, thereby affecting speeds and power distribution.

Two duplicate SSS clutches (Fig. 14.6) are placed on the aft end of the gearbox, the clutch for the F.T12 engine controlling the drive from the primary gear to the secondary pinion quill shaft, and the clutch for the FT4 engine controlling the input drive and primary F24 pinion. When on boost, the main wheel rotates the secondary pinion of the FT.12 and when on cruise, all the gears rotate, but only at cruise speed with low loss.

Fig. 7.31b shows the MAAG marine gear for this scheme in course of assembly, seated on a portion of the raft. The thrust collars on the secondary pinions are clearly shown.

The comparable machinery [64] for the Royal Navy is such that the boost and cruise engines can be arranged fore and aft of the main wheel. This extends the intake and exhaust ducting.

Good use has been made of this arrangement by the gear designers, Messrs David Brown Industries, Huddersfield, in having the boost and cruise turbines

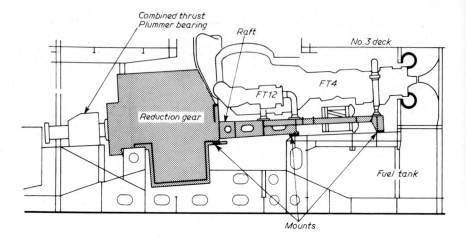

FIG. 7.30.—Machinery foundations—elevation for gas turbine-gear power package. All four engines are arranged forward of the gearcases and mounted on a raft with the gearcases. (R. M. Sachs, ASME 69–ST.26).

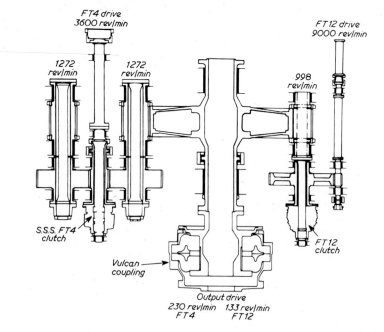

FIG. 7.31a.—Diagrammatic gear train arrangement for the Canadian DDH-280-Class gas turbine destroyers.

FIG. 7.31b.—MAAG marine gear for Canadian DDH-280-Class gas turbine destroyers in course of assembly, seated on a portion of the raft.

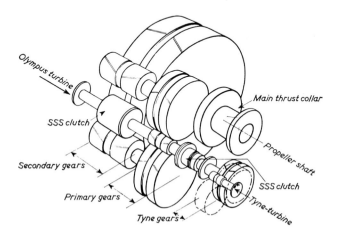

FIG. 7.32.—Rotating elements of Type 42 main gear box. (Beale and Gowans, I.Mar.E. **Trans.** 1970, Vol. 82–7).

driving the single primary pinion through SSS clutches on either side of the pinion, as in Fig. 7.32—Beale and Gowans.[37]

With this arrangement, none of the gears rotate unloaded when on boost or cruise. However, driving alternatively from each end of the pinion mismatches the mesh, which of course could be overcome by having a bearing-supported quill shaft for the cruise turbine, bolted to the other end of the pinion, thus having the same driving end for boost and cruise.

Double-helical gears are used and all are case-hardened, except the main wheel which is through-hardened and operates on a " hard-on-soft " basis.

These two examples show how the gear configuration is influenced by the disposition of the engines. They also show different conclusions regarding power turbine speeds. The choice of double-helical or single-helical gearing reflects the background of the gear designers. The raft mounting and associated Vulcan flexible coupling is referred to in the section on noise.

8. TYPES OF EPICYCLIC GEARS. BASIC FEATURES

Three main types of epicyclic gearing are established, Stoeckicht, Renk and MAAG, with a fourth being developed by Vickers.

In the first three, the planet pins are straddle-mounted on a rigid planet carrier and are precisely aligned to each other. If not, the load distribution across the face is affected, but not the load sharing. The sun pinion and the flexible annulus are centred by the planet wheels when under load. With the planetary arrangement, the planet carrier is bolted to the output shaft and can be supported in two bearings.

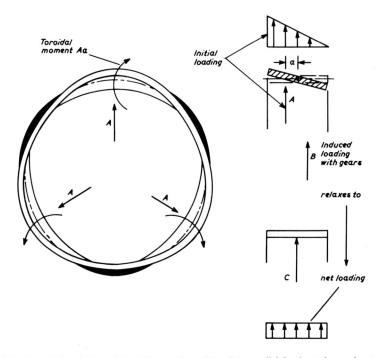

FIG. 8.1.—Toroidal twisting of flexible annulus with off-set radial load at three planet points. The effect with gears depends upon the method of supporting the annulus.

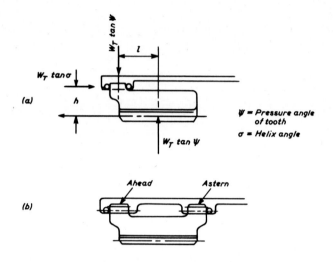

FIG. 8.2.—Externally supported annulus.
(a) Balance of axial couples on single helical annulus by positioning the external support.
(b) Scheme for reverse rotation with backlash on appropriate external teeth to take ahead or astern load.

With the ideally supported annulus, load-sharing between the planets is ensured by the radial flexibility, and uniform loading across the teeth by the self-correcting toroidal twisting of the annulus,[81] and of course the high accuracy of the gearing.

The self-correcting effect arises because non-uniform loading across the teeth twists the yielding annulus in the diametrical plane, thereby reducing the non-uniformity of the loading (Fig. 8.1). Small adjusting movements are sufficient.

The support problem is simple with spur gears, but with helical gears and separate annuli, the axial forces and couples introduced must be balanced to allow the self-correcting effect to come into play (Fig. 8.2.).

STOECKICHT

In the Stoeckicht system, double-helical gears are used with two separate annuli. The torque and thrust on the two annuli are taken by a helical gear tooth coupling which, in turn, is supported from the casing by an outer gear tooth coupling with straight teeth (Fig. 8.3a and b).

This allows the annuli assembly to move according to the misalignment between the planet carrier and the gear casing, giving the so-called " floating " effect.

With this system, forces and couples acting on each planet arise from the tangential, axial and radial forces, the latter two introducing toroidal moments on the annuli according to the position of their reaction forces.

These two can be balanced by shifting the external support-teeth, axially along the annulus, as shown in Fig. 8.2, so that the external radial and tangential moments, balance, i.e.:

$$l \cdot W_T \tan \psi = h \cdot W_T \tan \sigma$$

where W_T is the tangential force
ψ is the tangential pressure angle
σ is the helix angle
For ψ_n and σ equal to 20° and 30° respectively.

$$l \simeq 1 \cdot 5 \, h$$

For reversing, a similar set of teeth must be fitted at the other edge of the annulus, arranging the backlash so that the appropriate set of external teeth takes the load for ahead or astern. With such a balanced system, the self-correction can come into play, apart from friction.

With the current Allen-Stoeckicht design, the external teeth are placed centrally around the annulus and thereby introduce adverse toroidal moments at each planet which overcome the self-correction. This causes the two annuli to tilt inwards at the inside with apex leading, giving a higher load on the inside edges of the two annuli. This has been noted on meshing records.

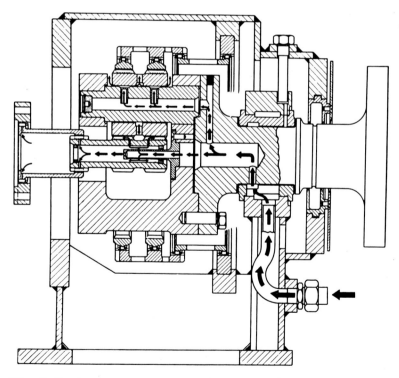

Fig. 8.3a.—Sectional arrangement of a typical Allen-Stoeckicht gear showing flow of lubricating oil.

Fig. 8.3b.—Principal components

(1) Planet wheel spindles   (5) High speed couplings
(2) Planet carrier   (6) Sun wheel
(3) Low speed shaft   (7) Planet wheels
(4) Annulus coupling rings   (8) Divided annulus.

Nevertheless, the Allen-Stoeckicht designs have had a remarkable success, showing the great importance of radial flexibility. Over 6×10^6 kW of ship power are in service with an availability of 99·6%

Figs. 8.4a, b and c shows the dismantling of a large Allen-Stoeckicht [93] gear. The gear has been swung on trunnions within the gearcase.

The planet pin assembly, annulus and output drive are clearly shown.

Fig. 8.5 shows an Allen-Stoeckicht triple-reduction epicyclic gear for 11 450 hp, 6550 rev/min driving a controllable pitch propeller at 112 rev/min.[72]

"Triple-reduction is used for economical reasons. The system adopted for the gears is a star first reduction, to avoid the centrifugal loads on the planet bearings, a star for the second reduction to give the correct relative rotation, and a planetary gear for the final reduction.

"The shaft brake is used to prevent rotation of the propeller when ship is being docked because of the relatively high idling torque of the heavy duty gas turbine"—Yates.[93]

RENK

In the Renk system (Fig. 8.6) double-helical gearing is used with two separate annuli which butt against each other. The annuli are resiliently supported from the casing by sleeve spring-packs, which permit both torsional and radial movement and, to some degree, angular movement in the diametrical plane, all of which are damped by the oil and friction within the spring-packs. The spring-packs can be chosen to suit the vibration characteristics required.

FIG. 8.4a, 4b.—Dismantling a large epicyclic gearbox
(W. H. Allen, Son & Co.).

Fig. 8.4c.—Dismantling a large epicyclic gearbox.
(W. H. Allen, Son & Co.).

Radial flexibility is a key factor in load sharing and it depends on the diameter of the annulus and the thickness of the metal between the radii at the bottom of the teeth and the semi-circle carrying the sleeve springs.

Toroidal twisting of the annuli is negligible. Uniform loading across the teeth is ensured by the high quality of the gearing, as has been proved on test and by service experience. Figs. 9.2a, b, and c show a Renk epicyclic gear for a diesel engine of 17 500 hp/417–137 rev/min.

MAAG

For high speed, MAAG use single-helical gears. The sun pinion is centred by the planets and the flexible extension shaft is supported in a bearing. The thrust from the sun pinion is preferably taken by the thrust bearing of the input power unit, against which it is balanced, or by thrust collars of the taper-land type, on one bearing.

A thin tubular extension, having a series of large holes, supports the flexible annulus from the casing, taking thrust and torque (Fig. 8.7a and b). It is clear that radial flexibility is the determining factor for load sharing. The toroidal twisting effect on the annulus is reduced to a minimum by having the tubular extension thin, and nearly in line with the axial thrust from the teeth.

Fig. 8.5.—Allen triple-reduction epicyclic main propulsion gearing for a G.E.(U.S.A.) heavy duty gas turbine of 11,450 hp/6550 rev/min driving a controllable pitch propeller at 112 rev/min. Figure shows the arrangement of the first, second, and final gear trains with top-half casings removed. Also shown, on the right, the auxiliary drives and in the foreground, the disc brake for the propeller shaft systems.

Fig. 8.8 shows a MAAG planetary gear for a diesel engine. As the pitch line velocity is relatively small, spur gears are chosen. This simplifies the annulus support problem. MAAG [76] have developed a series of standardised heavy-duty, epicyclic gears covering torque characteristics HP/N = 100 to 600.

All three types have been developed to a fine art and are well proven in industrial and marine service.

Another type is being developed by Vickers known as the " flexible pin type," invented by R. J. Hicks. This also has distinctive features.

Fig. 8.6.—Renk epicyclic gear with annulus supported in housing by sleeve springs.

Flexible planet pins are cantilevered from a single carrier plate with a planet bearing sleeve attached to the free end of the pin. The planet wheel runs on the bearing sleeve in the usual manner (Fig. 8.9). The deflection under normal load is considerably greater than the manufacturing errors, thus ensuring equality in load sharing, and the flexible pin is practically self-aligning in that the planets remain parallel to the annulus by deflection of the flexible pin, whether the first contact load is central or at one end of the pinion. This is true for tangential and radial loads from the sun and annulus, and since the deflection of the pin is influenced by both tangential and radial loads, it can compensate for skew of the planet.[79]

The sun wheel is floating and the annulus is radially stiff and rigidly attached to the outer casing, as in Fig. 8.10, hence the planets and sun wheel have to adjust themselves through each other to the rigid annulus.

With the single cantilever plate, the maximum number of planets can be used subject only to tip-to-tip clearance for any particular ratio. With straddle planet pins on rigid double carrier webs, the number of planets that can be carried is

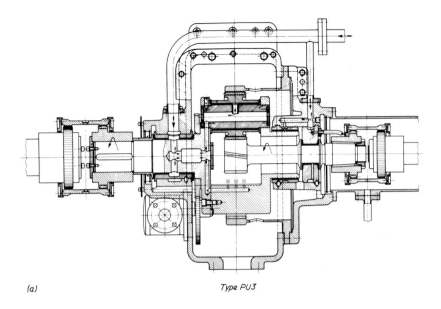

(a)   Type PU3

FIG. 8.7a.—MAAG single helical planetary gear.

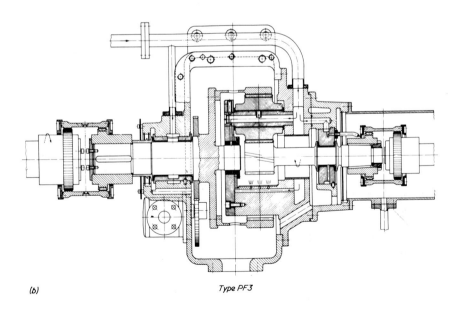

(b)   Type PF3

FIG. 8.7b.—MAAG single helical star gear.

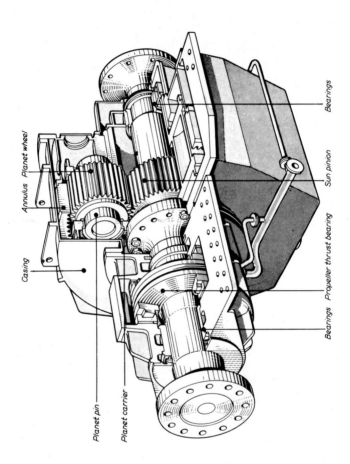

Fig. 8.8.—MAAG planetary gear for diesel drive.

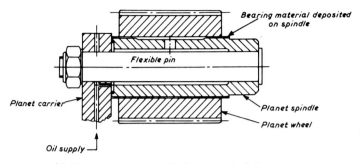

(a) Planet wheel rotates on flexibly mounted spindle

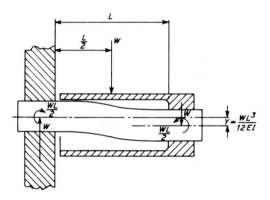

(b) Planet spindle loaded at centre

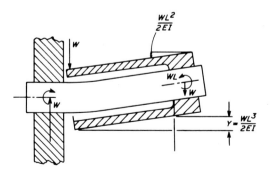

(c) Planet spindle loaded at end

Fig. 8.9.—Vickers flexible pin.

FIG. 8 10a.—Vickers standard marine epicyclic gear size MD 900.
(Beale and Gowans, I.Mar.E. Trans. Vol. 82, No. 7).

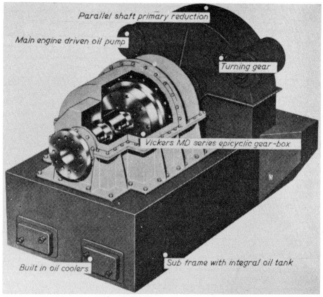

FIG. 8.10b.—Vickers standard final stage planetary gear combined with parallel shaft primary
gears for conventional cross-compound steam turbine installation. (Beale and Gowans,
I.Mar.E. Trans. Vol. 82, No. 7).

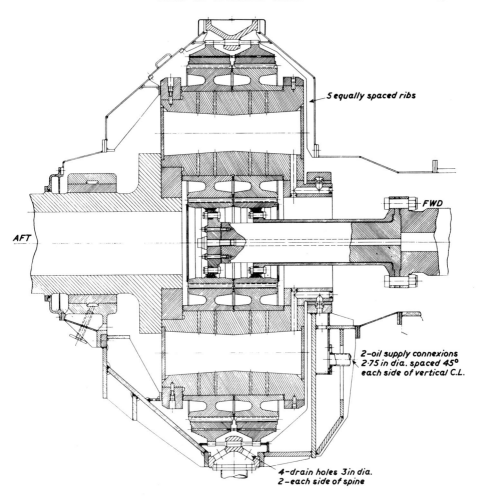

Fig. 8.11.—Paraplan secondary gear. (R. Coates Pametrada Standard Turbines. 1965. IES Ref. (72)).

limited slightly by the carrier construction. The difference in the number of planets is of little practical significance.

The development of the " flexible pin " type epicyclic gear will be watched with interest in its marine application, such as is shown in Figs. 8.10a and b.

In 1964, Pametrada designed a final reduction planetary gear which was to be associated with parallel primary gears for several input drives. Fig. 8.11 shows a section through the planetary gear. Important features are:

(a) double sun pinions, equally loaded through tuned quill shafts;
(b) straight spur teeth;
(c) flexible pin support of the two flexible annuli.

9. APPLICATION OF EPICYCLIC GEARING TO SINGLE DIESEL ENGINE DRIVE WITH REFERENCE TO HULL CONSTRUCTION FOR THRUST BLOCK AND ENGINE SUPPORT

For diesel engines, the epicyclic gear is admirably suited for single engine drives especially where the engines are placed well aft.

Such an arrangment is shown in Fig. 9.1 where the engine is so far aft that an epicyclic gear is the only solution. In this case, an M.A.N. reversible diesel engine of 17 500 hp at 417 rev/min with a light flywheel and flexible Vulcan coupling, coupled to a Renk planetary gear, drives a fixed pitch propeller at 137 rev/min.

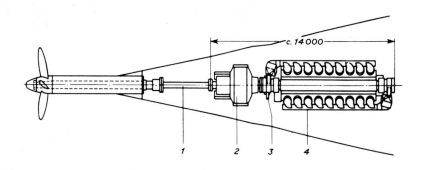

Fig. 9.1.—Extreme aft arrangements requiring a compact and very narrow reduction gear for which an epicyclic gear is most suitable.

As the propeller shaft line was extremely short special measures were taken in the design of the gear foundation. The top plate of the double bottom was enlarged to the full width of the hull at a height in line with the centre line of the shafting. The thrust block therefore was approximately "centre-line" mounted, so that the tilting movement caused by the propeller thrust would be minimised, and the longitudinal girders were extended underneath the gearbox to the machinery space.

Fig. 9.2a shows the size of the gear and Fig. 9.2b a section, in which it is seen that the sun pinion is floating on the three planet wheels. The annulus is connected to the gear housing by "sleeve" spring-packs. Fig. 9.1 shows the four bearings in the shaft alignment and Fig. 9.2c shows the assembling of the gearbox. Axial

FIG. 9.2a.—Renk planetary marine gear for 17,500 hp and 417-137 rev/min.

vibrations from the propeller getting through the main thrust block are taken up by the axial sliding of the planets on their pins, thereby isolating the mesh from these external forces. This is a special feature of all epicyclic gears.

Where there is more than one engine, a parallel shaft gear is always used. For lower powered engines, the pinion centres are determined by the engine centre distance, when they are installed side by side. The gears therefore are lightly loaded.

This makes possible an ideal solution to the problem of misalignment, as shown in a further example by Renk [63] illustrating other important features. The gear-case and rotating elements are made symmetrical (Fig. 9.3). The thrust block is separate and is " centre-line " mounted and has no journal bearings. A four-point support is used on the axes of symmetry and each engine, with a flexible Vulcan coupling, drives a quill shaft which is taken through the hollow pinion to a separately supported friction clutch, from which a gear-tooth coupling drives the pinion. The support system is shown in Fig. 9.4. In this scheme, the multi-disc clutch serves to connect or disconnect either engine with the propeller, which is a requirement with multi-engine reduction gears. The operational characteristics of the Renk clutch, it is stated, are " compatible with the requirements of clutch-in and clutch-out manoeuvres, even under extreme crash-stop conditions."

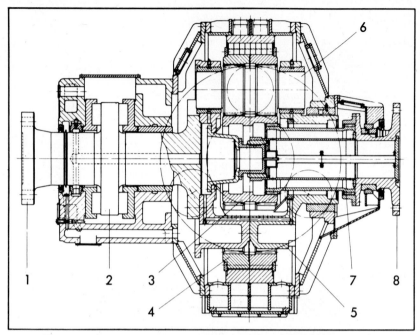

FIG. 9.2b.—Sectional arrangement through Renk planetary marine type gear.

FIG. 9.2c.—Gear train of planetary marine gear Renk PAS 180p in course of assembly.

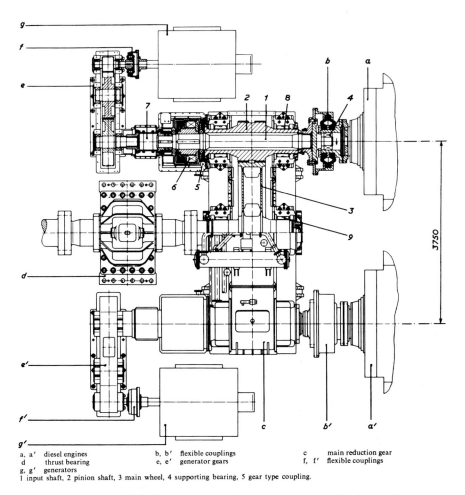

a, a' diesel engines   b, b' flexible couplings   c   main reduction gear
d   thrust bearing   e, e' generator gears   f, f' flexible couplings
g, g' generators
1 input shaft, 2 pinion shaft, 3 main wheel, 4 supporting bearing, 5 gear type coupling.

FIG. 9.3.—17·2 MW (23,400 hp) marine reduction gear installed with other machinery.

Fig. 9.5 shows the drive for a twin diesel, with a combined resilient coupling-pneumatic-friction clutch, as used by other manufacturers. The symmetric design and mounting of the Renk scheme is similar to that used by Stal Laval (Fig. 7.11).

With larger powered, medium speed engines, used in pairs side by side, with propeller speeds of about 90 rev/min, the pinion centres, with normal soft-on-soft gearing, would determine the engine centre distance. In fact, to maintain minimum centre distance between two engines, locked train gears have been proposed (T. Takahashi—Mar. Eng. and Nav. Assn. June 1971). However, as proposed by Sigg " The use of coarse pitches in marine propulsion gearing "—8th Round Table

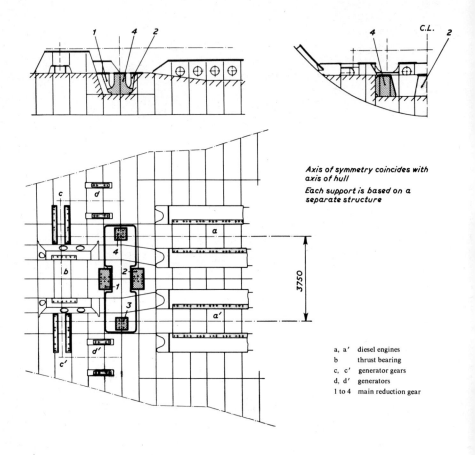

Axis of symmetry coincides with
axis of hull

Each support is based on a
separate structure

a, a′   diesel engines
b   thrust bearing
c, c′   generator gears
d, d′   generators
1 to 4   main reduction gear

FIG. 9.4.—Arrangement of machinery supports. (Pinnekamp I.Mar.E. Trans. 1975, Vol. 87).

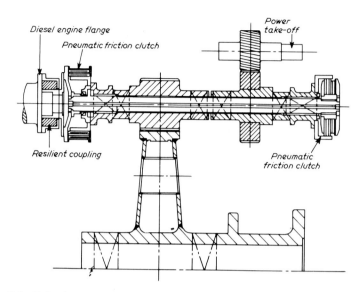

FIG. 9.5.—Drive for diesel propulsion, incorporating power take-off gear. (G.E.C.(U.K.)).

Conf. on Marine Gearing 1972—straight-forward, single-reduction gearing can be used with surface-hardened and ground pinions, and ground gear at (75–85 tons/in², 120–135 kg/mm²) i.e. hard-on-soft, but with larger pitches than those commonly used in marine application. This is so outstanding that the essentials are given below.

For the tanker application the conditions were:

Maximum continuous power per engine	27 000 hp/370 rev/min
Propeller speed	90 rev/min
Minimum centre distance between two engines side by side	5000 mm.
Normal module M_n	22·5 mm (p_n = 2·77 inch)
Helix angle	8° − 0·8
Face width	820 mm
Load per inch W_{if}	7350 lb
Lloyds K factor	235
Specific tooth bending stress $\dfrac{W_{if}}{P_n}$	2650 lb/in²

MAAG have considerable experience with gears of large tooth pitch, under service conditions more arduous than those occurring in marine applications.[76]

10. REVERSING—MECHANICS OF REVERSING WITH STEAM TURBINES

An understanding of the mechanics of reversing is required to appreciate how the transient loads come on to the gearing and also the precautions which must be taken with the reversing system.

The most effective way of stopping, or reversing, a ship is to use the maximum astern power available as soon as possible.[82] The amount of power and the speed with which it is applied greatly influences the transient torques and thrust from the propeller. The speed of the ship, its mass and resistance, the engine and means of reversing, all operate on the propeller. The characteristics of the propeller are usually shown as Robinson curves, giving thrust and torque on a base of ahead and astern rev/min obtained at constant forward speeds of the vessel (Fig. 10.1a). The results can also be given as non-dimensional coefficients (Fig. 10.1b). The torque and thrust curves are similar in form because they are components of the resultant force acting on the propeller.

Consider reversing with a steam turbine set. Usually the astern steam turbine is about 50% of the full ahead power, giving a torque characteristic of 65% at full speed astern to 100% at stall as a percentage of the full ahead torque. This extends into the ahead rev/min region, giving over 100% resistance torque when the astern steam is applied (Fig. 10.2a). The resistance of the astern turbine is of course only a small percentage when running ahead under vacuum.

When the order to bring the ship to stop is given, the ahead throttle is shut and astern throttle opened in 20 to 30 seconds. During this time the propeller speed slows down to about 70% of full speed and the ship speed falls at a slower rate. When the astern turbine power takes effect, the propeller speed is reduced still further, creating increased propeller torques and thrusts due to the ship's motion as shown by the Robinson curves (Fig. 10.2a). The position on the Robinson curves will show the stopping torque of the astern turbine, plus frictional resistance to the shafting, to be greater than the propeller torque. The irregularities in torque and rev/min can be followed by comparing the plots of the conditions against time (Fig. 10.2b) and against rev/min (Fig. 10.2a).

The first peak before the propeller stops is the stalling torque and is followed by a drop in torque. This drop occurs on all aero and hydrofoils in various degrees and can be the cause of stalling flutter, cavitation and noise. No loss in the grip of the marine propeller ever occurs in this area.

The second major torque peak occurs when the propeller is running in reverse and the ship is still going forward. The maximum occurs when the water flows at

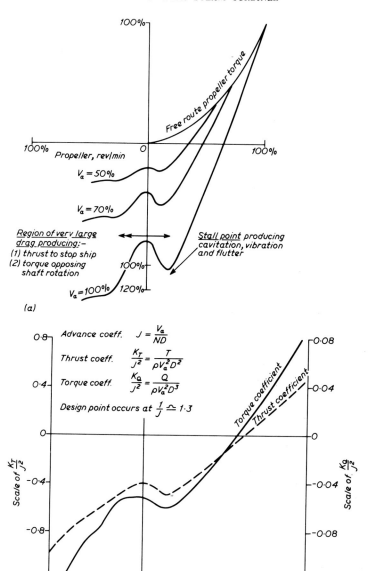

FIG. 10.1a.—Robinson curves of propeller torque with constant forward velocities. Similar curves are obtained for thrust.

FIG. 10.1b.—Plotted as non-dimensional coefficients.

FIG. 10.1.—Propeller characteristics.

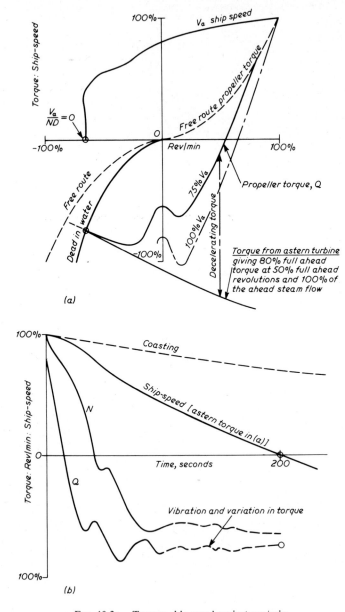

(a)

(b)

Fig. 10.2a.—Torque; ship-speed against rev/min.

Fig. 10.2b.—Torque; rev/min; ship-speed against time.

Fig. 10.2.—Reversing characteristics.

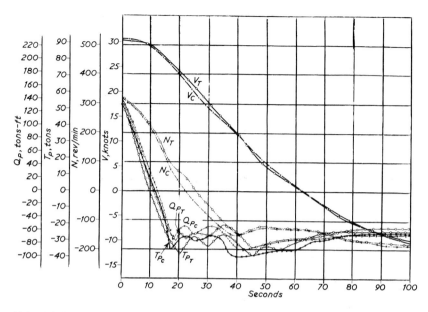

Fig. 10.3.—HMS *Savage*—Full ahead to full astern. (Goodwin *et al.* I.Mar.E. Trans. Vol. **80**, No. 7).

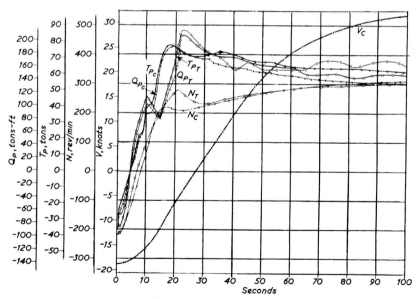

Fig. 10.4.—HMS *Savage*—Full astern to full ahead. (Goodwin *et al.* I.Mar.E. Trans. Vol. **80**, No. 7).

right angles to the blades at which point the drag is a maximum and, so, also its components of thrust and torque.

In this region the propeller can exceed the engine torque, causing the shaft to slow down, during which time the ship slows down and the propeller torque reduces until it is less than the engine torque when the shaft is accelerated again. The peak torques can be up to 100% full load torque which, for a cross-compound set with the astern turbine in the L.P. cylinder, would give overtorques in the L.P. gear train up to 200%. This would be for a crash stop, with which all means of reversing must be capable of dealing, as well as the normal duty of repeated manoeuvres.

With vibration occurring during reversal, there would most probably be tooth separation in the unloaded H.P. turbine gears, with consequent gear-hammer and noise. These effects are influenced by the torsional vibration characteristics of the branched system and are usually well within the tooth capacity.

Figs. 10.3 and 10.4 show the conditions for full ahead to full astern and for full astern to full ahead in a naval vessel—Goodwin [76]—with an astern power about 1/3 of the full ahead power.

11. REVERSING WITH DIESEL ENGINES

These excess propeller torques cannot be permitted with diesel engines, other-wise the engines would stall. A delay period must, therefore, be allowed, for the ship to slow down.

This again can be seen from the Robinson curves given by Lea (Fig. 11.1).

If friction clutches are fitted, these must be capable of transmitting the maximum torque of the engine without slipping and must be able to overcome the propeller torque during the arresting period which is of the order of 10 seconds. During this period they must be capable of dissipating the slip-horsepower. The heat rate input to the clutches during the slipping period is a function of the clutch torque and the speed differential between the engaging clutches and their discs. Thus heat rate is:

$$(\mu p A r)(\omega_1 - \omega_2) \equiv hp$$
where μ is the friction coefficient
p is the pressure on the pads in lb/in^2
A is the area of the pads
ω is the angular velocity.

Fig. 11.2a shows the results from a test on a " shore trials " shaft brake. It will be noticed that the torque curve follows that of the fluid pressure. Fig. 11.2b shows the heat rate and the total heat by integrating over the slipping period. The measured temperature of the disc is also given.

The hp/in^2 of pad area was $2 \cdot 58$ mean and $6 \cdot 8$ maximum for about 15 seconds and 3 seconds respectively.

Practical values for long life with repeated brakings are of the order of $0 \cdot 5$ hp/in^2 mean, depending on whether the clutch is oil immersed, or dry, and the type of material.

The Falk Corporation, USA, have developed a Marine Airflex Clutch, the 48 inch diameter single element of which has a capacity of the same order as the above disc clutch and is shown in Fig. 11.3.

The Falk clutches [88] have been used on a 25 000 hp/3850—145 rev/min single input gas turbine drive as described by Richardson.[88] As shown in Fig. 11.4, two clutch units, each with three elements in parallel, are used for ahead and a similar pair for astern.

Developments are proceeding with large capacity brakes for which Dunlop Limited has testing equipment giving 120×10^6 ft lb. brake energy [96] i.e. 10

91

times that used on the "shore trials" set. Their carbon-fibre brake assembly is new technology.

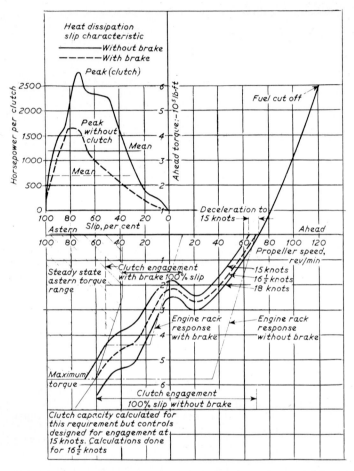

FIG. 11.1.—Torque-propeller speed characteristics of 26,000 tonnes displacement during full astern manoeuvres from 13,600 shp provided by two kV-16 major engines. (Goodwin *et al.* I.Mar.E. Trans. Vol. 80, No. 7).

The delay period is vital with diesel engine, friction clutch manoeuvring, as much as 80 seconds delay being required before operating the clutches.[82, 85] In cases of emergency, with any means of shaft reversal, this could be an exciting, but helpless, period. However, special stopping manoeuvres are being developed by B.S.R.A. on large steam turbine tankers, where the rudder is cycled between hard to port and hard to starboard, about ± 40°, at a calculated frequency. " The basic philosophy is to obtain the maximum drag from the hull during yawing and

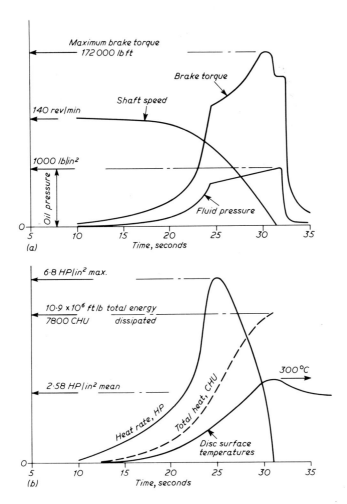

Fig. 11.2.—Extreme test on a propeller shaft disc brake. 4'6" dia-1" thick with 14 double pads.

from the rudder at large angles of attack. This reduces the head reach considerably while controlling the path of the ship to a large extent." [94] A reduction in head reach of 45% was achieved, compared with a crash stop from the same initial conditions.

This principle is used with twin rudders where the steering control system [95] moves the twin rudders hard over outboard, thus creating the maximum forward resistance. These methods are most effective at the high speed end of the speed scale and is just what is required during the engine delay period.

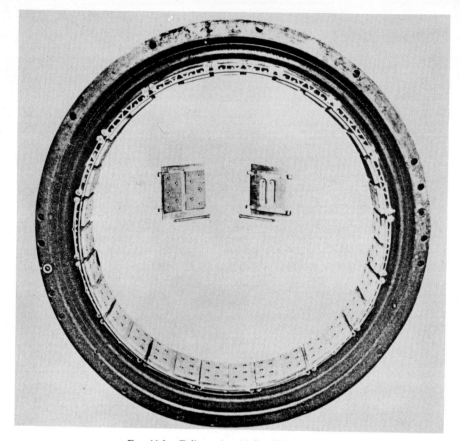

FIG. 11.3.—Falk marine Airflex Clutch Element.

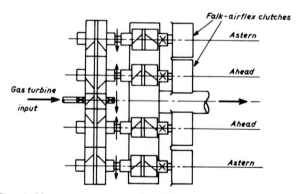

FIG. 11.4.—Gas turbine reverse gear arrangement with Falk airflex friction clutches.
(W. S. Richardson, Falk Corpn. (82) 1967).

In conjunction with the equations of motion for the machinery given in Fig. 12.2, the ship's motion is given by:

$$M \frac{dv}{dt} = T_P - R - \text{rudder braking}$$

where M is the mass of the ship
v is the velocity of the ship
R is the resistance of the ship
T_P is the propeller thrust.

With c.p. propellers, delay techniques are again applied, as before, and for the additional precaution of preventing overspeed of the shafting at low torques. No excessive loading comes on the gearing, with c.p. propellers, when using the correct control.

12. REVERSING WITH GAS TURBINES

Reversing gas turbines are predicted for the future but at present this function is normally performed by c.p. propellers, or a reversing gear.

When the Royal Navy County Class and Tribal Class vessels were introduced, there was no c.p. propeller of the power required for the combined unit, so it was necessary to develop a reversing gear for the gas turbine. This consisted of two similar fluid couplings, the astern one driving through an idler gear. Ahead and astern manoeuvring was achieved by selectively emptying and filling the appropriate fluid coupling (Fig. 12.1). Fig. 12.2 shows the characteristics of the various components as measured by strain gauges and torque meters during a reversal, and Fig. 12.3 shows the corresponding ship speed, rev/min, torque and coupling oil temperature on a base of time.

Should the shaft be held, or stalled at zero speed, all the gas turbine power must be absorbed in the fluid couplings with a consequent rise in oil temperature. This heat is taken away immediately in the lubricating oil, and the throughput of oil can be adjusted to suit the particular installation.

All means of reversing must be capable of dealing with the " crash stop " from full ahead, and the normal duty of repeated manoeuvres. During a " crash stop " from full ahead, with any system of reversing, a sudden reversal of full engine torque would introduce greater propeller thrust and torque than the steady values at various speeds of advance, and probably greater than the peak torque of the engine or stalling torque of the turbine. A time delay is arranged by reducing the engine power, thereby getting the benefit of the maximum resistance of the ship before applying reverse power, which may be by reversing gear with fluid couplings/friction clutches, or c.p. propellers.

Fig. 12.4 shows this effect, with fluid couplings and gas turbines, measured during the sea trials of machinery for the Tribal Class vessels. This gives propeller torque on a base of rev/min, and is compared with the normal delay periods from other ships. These high torques, of an impactive nature, are taken by the gearing.

Larger powers are envisaged with the use of two or three large gas turbines driving one propeller shaft, e.g. 50 000 and 75 000 shp respectively at, say, 160 rev/min. This is beyond the capacity of c.p. propellers at present, reversing, therefore, has to be achieved in the gearbox. Again, schemes with fluid couplings and idlers are clearly the best solution. Fig. 12.5a and b shows a compact arrangement by SSS Gears Ltd. with a twin gas turbine input driving a single propeller [90] giving 50 000 shp at about 160 rev/min.

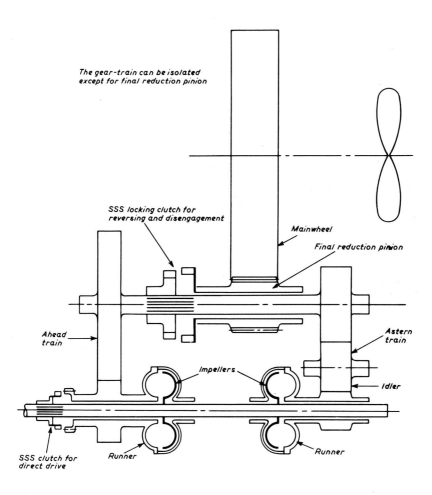

The gear-train can be isolated
except for final reduction pinion

SSS locking clutch for
reversing and disengagement

Mainwheel

Final reduction pinion

Ahead
train

Astern
train

Impellers

Idler

SSS clutch for
direct drive

Runner

Runner

FIG. 12.1.—Outline of hydraulic coupling reversing gear on Y102 (see Fig. 4.3).

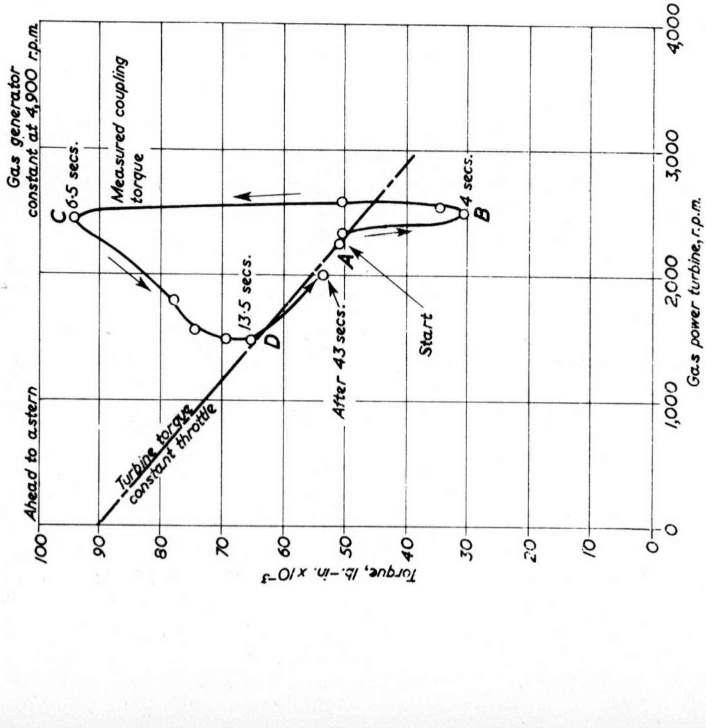

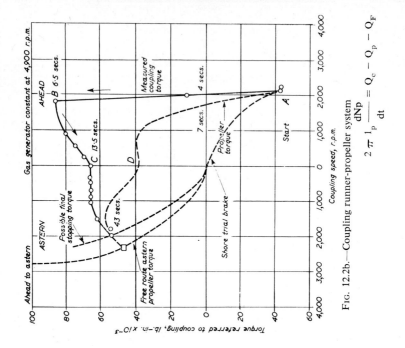

Fig. 12.2b.—Coupling runner-propeller system

$$2 \pi\, I_p\, \frac{dN_p}{dt} = Q_c - Q_p - Q_F$$

Fig. 12.2a.—Power turbine-coupling system equation of motion

$$I_{t\,c}\, \frac{dN_E}{dt} = Q_E - Q_C$$

Fig. 12.2.—Measured torques during reversal.

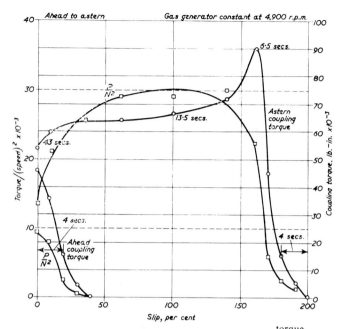

FIG. 12.2c.—Strain gauge torque measurement of couplings and $\dfrac{\text{torque}}{(\text{speed})^2}$ versus slip.

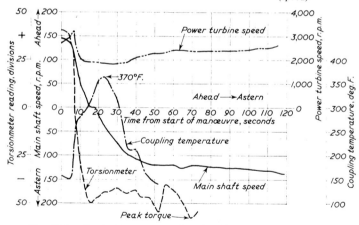

FIG. 12.3.—Gas turbine manoeuvring ahead/astern—HMS *Ashanti*.
(I. M. Dunlop and E. B. Good. I.Mar.E. Trans. Vol. 75. No. 1).

where $I_{t.c.}$ is the moment of inertia of the power turbine-coupling impeller system
I_p is the moment of inertia of the coupling runner-propeller system
N_E is the power turbine speed Q_c is the coupling torque
N_P is the propeller speed Q_p is the propeller torque
Q_E is the power turbine torque Q_F is the friction torque on the shafting system

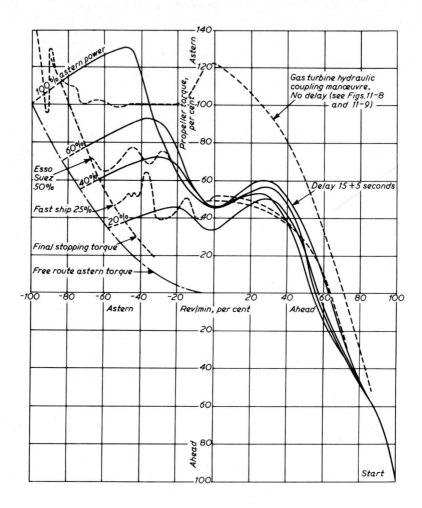

FIG. 12.4.—Propeller torque and rev/min during stopping of ship from full ahead power for various values of astern power.

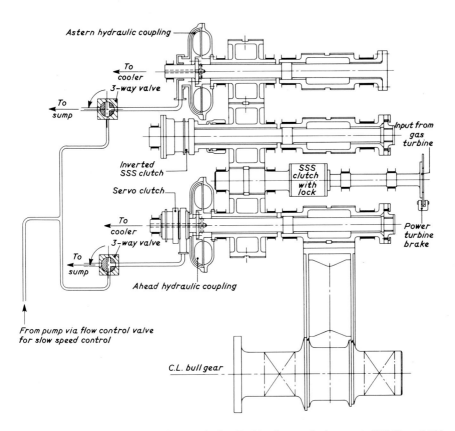

FIG. 12.5a.—Marine Manoeuvring Gear Twin Gas Turbine input—single output. (SSS Gears Ltd.).

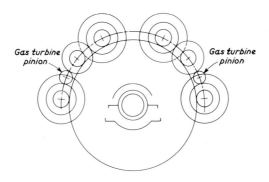

FIG. 12.5b.—Marine Manoeuvring Gear Twin Gas Turbine input—single output.

For the larger powers, the fluid couplings are best installed on the intermediate shafts, as shown, as this permits the best choice of speed, coupling size and a reduction of centrifugal stresses in the couplings, and also in the number of high speed bearings.

With multiple engines, all but one can be shut off for efficient cruising, hence it is desirable to isolate these engines completely, except for their final pinions; this would require an automatic SSS clutch on each of the final reduction pinions. It will be noted that an inverted SSS clutch is incorporated. This clutch, when engaged, automatically drives the ahead and astern coupling at zero and 200% slip respectively. As there is no operating oil in the fluid couplings at this time, the windage, as proven by tests, gives a power loss of less than 0·25% of the turbine power. This makes schemes, such as shown in Fig. ~~11.11~~ 12.5a, a practical proposition.

13. REVERSING WITH EPICYCLIC GEARING

Reversing with epicyclic gearing requires two gear trains, cross-connected and operated by ahead and astern brakes, or fluid couplings.

The method used by W. H. Allen Son and Co. in HMS *Brave Borderer*—a high speed patrol boat—is shown in Fig. 13.1a.

Here the annulus A_1 of the first gear is connected to the sun S_2 of the second gear, and the carrier C_1 of the first gear is connected to the annulus A_2 of the second gear. The input is to S_1 and the output from S_2 as shown in Fig. 13.1b.

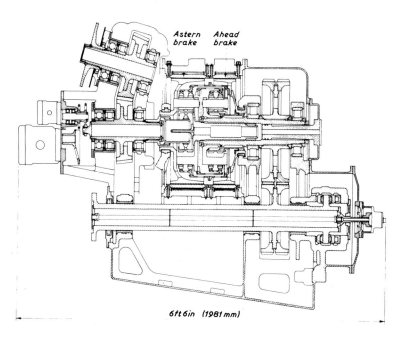

Astern brake Ahead brake

6ft 6in (1981 mm)

FIG. 13.1a.—Reverse/reduction epicyclic gear for a fast patrol boat. (W. H. Allen).

103

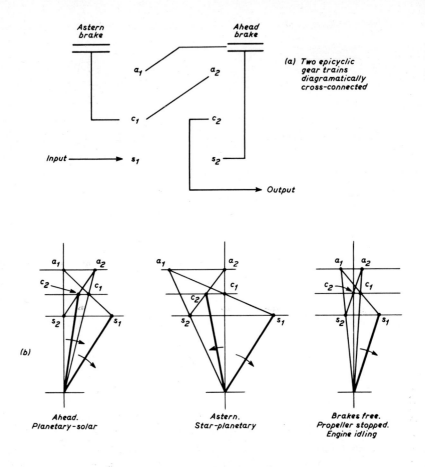

FIG. 13.1b.—Velocity diagrams for reverse/reduction epicyclic gear.

The velocity diagrams are shown for ahead and astern, and also, with the brakes free, the propeller stopped and the turbine idling.

It is to be noted that all the gears are loaded when driving ahead or astern. For equal ahead and astern gear ratios, the overall ratio is about 4·2. The annuli for HMS *Brave Borderer* was 12-inch diameter and the power transmitted was 3500 hp. Due to the increased resistance of the high speed craft as it settles in the water, the energy dissipated during a reversal is relatively small and oil operated clutches are used.

For larger displacement vessels, it is necessary to use air-cooled dry friction brakes outside the gearbox. Fig. 13.2 shows an Allen reverse/reduction epicyclic gearbox for 11 000 kW, with external braking.[93]

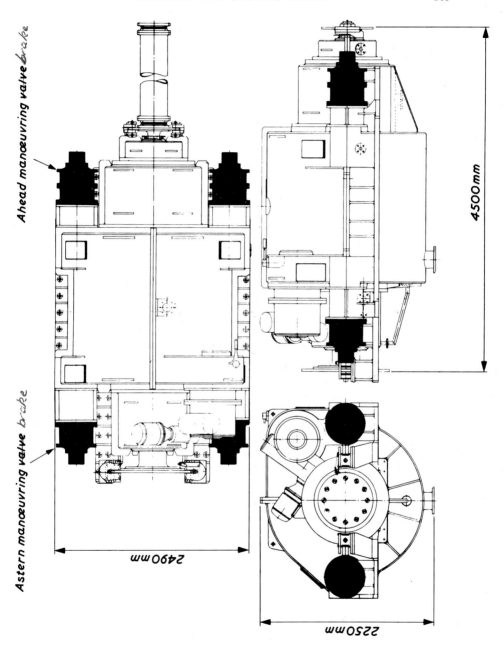

Ahead manoeuvring valve brake

Astern manoeuvring valve brake

2490mm

4500mm

2250mm

FIG. 13.2.—An Allen reverse/reduction epicyclic gearbox for 11,000 kW with external braking. (Yates).

14. SSS CLUTCHES

An outstanding development in gearing for combined plants is the Synchronous-Self-Shifting clutch which engages automatically at the instant the speed of the input shaft tends to overtake that of the output, and conversely disengages as soon as the output side runs faster than the input.

The load is taken by normal involute teeth which are shifted precisely into engagement exactly at synchronism by means of a pawl-actuated helical sliding sleeve. When the pawls on one clutch element engage with the ratchet teeth on the other element, the driving teeth are precisely aligned with the spaces between the driven teeth for inter-engagement (Fig. 14.1).

Hence when the speeds of the shafts pass through synchronism, the pawls move the sliding component along the helical splines, thereby engaging the driving and driven teeth, smoothly. During this movement, the pawls pass out of engagement with the ratchet teeth into the free position and therefore do not transmit any driving torque, the only load on the pawls being that required to shift the light-weight helical sliding sleeve.

The driving teeth complete the axial movement of the sliding member which finally abuts against: (a) the end face B, like a nut on a bolt, or (b) against a rotational stop on the outer circumference of the sliding member. With (a) the load is taken by the helical splines, and with (b) the helical splines are unloaded.

To prevent impact and rebound on reaching the stops, a dashpot is incorporated in the sliding member which is powerful enough to accelerate the slower member and decelerate the faster member so that a gentler contact is made.

A further development on this clutch includes the use of two rows of pawls, one set being effective when the shafts are at rest or at low speed, the other being effective when the output shaft is rotating at higher speeds under the action of the other engine. The low speed set of pawls are carried by the output parts of the clutch and these pawls are centrifugally disengaging whilst the high speed set of pawls are carried by the input side of the clutch and these centrifugally engage. With such a double set of pawls, at least one set will always be effective to engage the clutch, at any speed from zero to maximum speed, but both sets of pawls are inert when the clutch output is at high speed and the input stopped or at low speed.

For high power high speed clutches, a relay system of two helical sliding members is used, the lightweight smaller clutch is first shifted into tooth engagement by pawls, then the teeth of this smaller clutch shifts the larger main clutch into engagement.

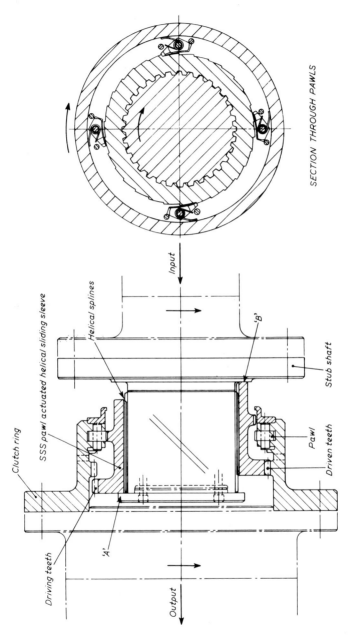

Clutch ring

SSS pawl actuated helical sliding sleeve

Helical splines

Driving teeth

'A'

Output

Input

SECTION THROUGH PAWLS

'B'

Stub shaft

Pawl

Driven teeth

FIG. 14.1.—Basic action in the Synchronous-Self-Shifting tooth engagement.

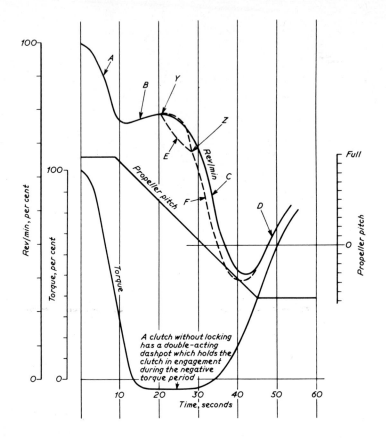

F<small>IG</small>. 14.2.—SSS clutch conditions during manoeuvre from full ahead to full astern with CPP propeller. (Clements).

CLUTCHES WITH C.P. PROPELLERS

In unidirectional marine gas turbine applications such as when the c.p. propeller is used, the SSS clutch can be a simple arrangement since it acts as an overrunning clutch.

During " crash astern " manoeuvres, a small negative torque can occur for a few seconds (Fig. 14.2), hence a powerful double-acting dashpot is fitted with controlled oil feed which holds the clutch axially in engagement during the negative torque period. The oil is turned off simultaneously with the shutting down of the associated engine to permit the clutch to disengage. However, even if disengagement does take place during manoeuvring, the clutch with re-engage a few seconds later, which is perfectly acceptable. With unidirectional clutches, a

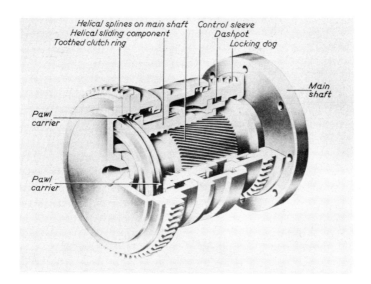

FIG. 14.3.—SSS clutch with lock control, giving pawl free position. For shaft end mounting, in series with toothed flexible coupling.

manual method of locking out the clutch is incorporated to permit engine testing without rotating the gearing.

CLUTCHES WITH FIXED PITCH PROPELLERS

If the SSS clutch is used with a fixed-pitch propeller, it is required, after automatic engagement, to transmit power in an astern as well as in an ahead direction of rotation. This requires a locking sleeve to lock the clutch in the " engaged-position ", as shown in Fig. 14.3. This is the type used in the Royal Navy County Class and Tribal Class vessels. Fig. 14.3 shows the general principles:

    (a) pawls free—clutch bi-directionally free;
    (b) pawls engaged—clutch overrunning;
    (c) clutch engaged—unlocked;
    (d) clutch engaged—and locked bi-directionally.

A baulk mechanism can be incorporated in the clutch, to prevent it from being shifted from the pawls free position, when the clutch output is rotating astern relative to the input, otherwise instant damage to the pawls and ratchets will occur.

Fig. 14.5 shows the dynamic conditions during engagement.

CLUTCH MOUNTING

Mounting arrangements are important. Fig. 14.6 shows a preferred arrangement with quill shaft drive, which can be used on either high or intermediate speed shafts. Nevertheless with high speed gas turbine drives requiring long

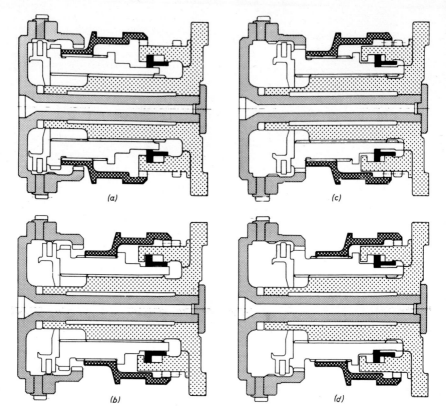

FIG. 14.4a.—Pawls free—clutch bi-directionally free.
FIG. 14.4b.—Pawls engaged. Clutch overrunning.
FIG. 14.4c.—Clutch engaged. Unlocked.
FIG. 14.4d.—Clutch engaged. Locked bi-directionally

FIG. 14.4.—Operation of SSS Clutch with locking control.

torque tubes with membrane couplings, vibration can occur at the outboard
bearing as a whip effect due to mounting conditions of the turbine at the other
end of the running line.[135a]

Fig. 14.7 shows a typical mounting of SSS clutches when two turbines are
driving a single high speed pinion. Here the clutches are made self-supporting by
means of a drum surrounding the complete clutch, giving a two, external-journal,
bearing support and a better chance of dealing with vibration problems should
they arise.

In the Royal Navy County and Tribal Class vessels, the SSS clutch was similar
to Fig. 14.8 and fitted to an intermediate shaft line. This meant that the whole of

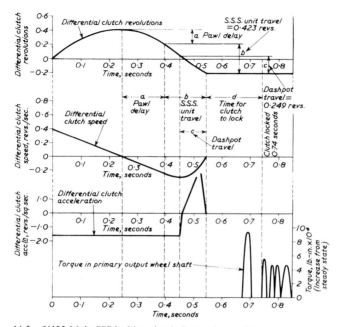

Fig. 14.5.—Y102 Main SSS locking clutch. Dynamic conditions during engagement.

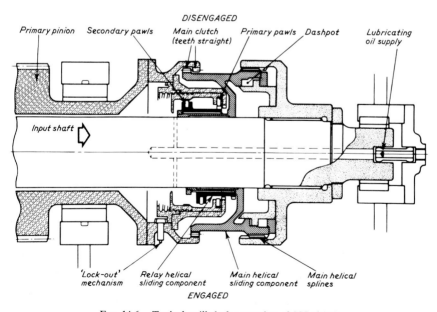

Fig. 14.6.—Typical quill shaft mounting of SSS clutch.

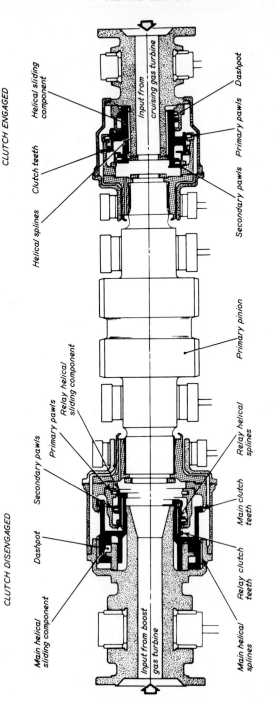

CLUTCH ENGAGED

Helical sliding
component

Dashpot

Primary pawls

Clutch teeth

Secondary pawls

Helical splines

CLUTCH DISENGAGED

Primary pinion

Relay helical
sliding component

Primary pawls

Relay helical
splines

Secondary pawls

Main clutch
teeth

CLUTCH DISENGAGED

Dashpot

Relay clutch
teeth

Main helical
sliding component

Main helical
splines

CLUTCH ENGAGED

Input from
cruising gas turbine

Input from boost
gas turbine

Fig. 14.7.—Typical mounting of SSS clutches when two turbines are driving a single pinion.

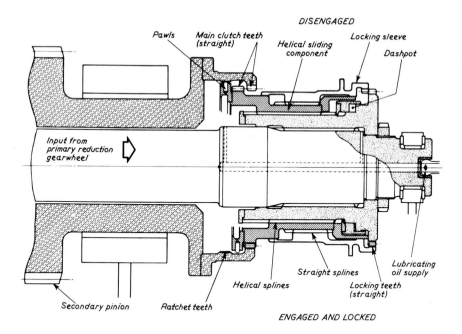

DISENGAGED

Pawls

Main clutch teeth
(straight)

Helical sliding
component

Locking sleeve

Dashpot

Input from
primary reduction
gearwheel

Lubricating
oil supply

Straight splines

Locking teeth
(straight)

Helical splines

Secondary pinion

Ratchet teeth

ENGAGED AND LOCKED

FIG. 14.8.—Typical mounting of SSS clutch on an intermediate shaft.

the high speed gearing could be disconnected while the vessel continued to be propelled by another engine. This makes the system more reliable, as the effects of unbalance, due to clearances in the clutch locking sleeve and other parts, are considerably decreased, also the associated running line is free from critical speeds.

15. MAAG SYNCHRONOUS CLUTCH COUPLING

The MAAG synchronous clutch coupling is a straightforward gear tooth coupling with mechanical synchronising. One type, used with unidirectional gears, engages and disengages automatically as an overrunning clutch (Fig. 15.1) and another is fitted with a servo-mechanism which locks the clutch after automatic engagement, making it insensitive to torque reversal (Fig. 15.2).

The spool of the coupling has a set of external teeth permanently engaged in an internally toothed sleeve, in which it slides axially when the set of teeth at the other end of the spool are engaged with a second internally toothed sleeve attached to the shaft to be engaged.

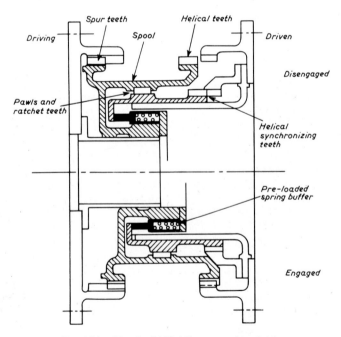

Fig. 15.1.—Sketch of MAAG overrunning clutch.

The synchronising mechanism, working inside the spool, consists of a sleeve with external ratchet teeth at one end and external diamond shaped teeth at the other, the latter being permanently engaged in the helical portion of a part helical/part spur gear, on the inside of the toothed sleeve on the shaft to be engaged. The part spur gear portion is omitted when the overrunning clutch is used.

The ratchet sleeve is centred on a shaft extension and is located axially with the coupling spool, by a spring loaded buffer (Fig. 15.1).

The pawls are rectangular in shape and are loosely contained with circumferential clearance in rectangular chambers on the inside of the spool, in which they can tilt. Below synchronous speed, the ratchet teeth rotate under the pawls, separated by a hydrodynamic oil film. With rotation of the driving system, the pawls tilt favourably by centrifugal force, on to the ratchet wheel, maintaining the hydrodynamic oil film.

When the driving system overruns the driven, one pawl abuts immediately against one of the ratchet teeth—the impact being reduced by the springs in accordance with their preloading—and the ratchet wheel, together with the gear coupling, is shifted in a screw motion, along with the helical gear element, getting the chamfered ends of the spool teeth into meshing position, but without touching the mating teeth.

With the locking clutch, a servo-mechanism pushes the spool teeth axially into full engagement. During this axial movement, the ratchet wheel carries out an

FIG. 15.2.   MAAG Synchronous clutch coupling with locking.

Fig. 15.3.—MAAG synchronous clutch coupling components showing
(a) part spool with internal pawl chambers
(b) ratchet wheel and pawls and synchronising teeth
(c) internally toothed sleeve with part helical—part spur teeth for locking coupling

additional small screw motion which withdraws the pawls circumferentially from
the ratchet teeth, after which the driving teeth make contact, transmitting the
torque only through the tooth coupling. In the final position the coupling is
insensitive to torque reversal.

With the overrunning clutch, the engaging teeth on the clutch are helical and,
just where they take over from the helical teeth on the ratchet wheel, the pawls
are automatically withdrawn circumferentially from the ratchet wheel teeth by
the differential screw motion, so that there is no load on the pawls. The torque
on the helical teeth of the clutch spool moves the spool into full engagement on
coming to a hydraulic stop against the shaft abutment.

The relative positions of the teeth are shown in Fig. 15.4, for the successive
stages of engagement.

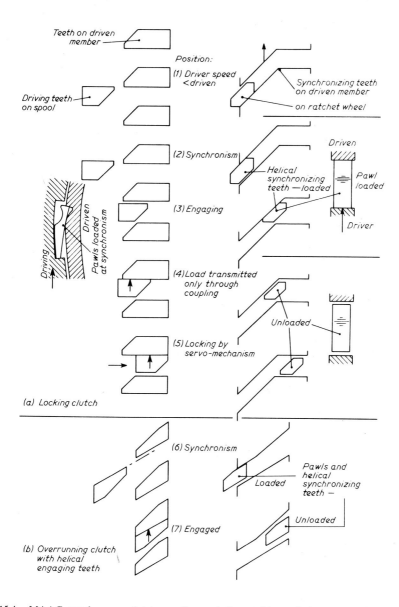

Teeth on driven member

Position:

(1) Driver speed <driven

Driving teeth on spool

Synchronizing teeth on driven member

on ratchet wheel

(2) Synchronism

Driven

Helical synchronizing teeth —loaded

Pawl loaded

(3) Engaging

Driver

Driving

Driven

Pawls loaded at synchronism

(4) Load transmitted only through coupling

Unloaded

(5) Locking by servo-mechanism

(a) Locking clutch

(6) Synchronism

Loaded

Pawls and helical synchronizing teeth —

Unloaded

(7) Engaged

(b) Overrunning clutch with helical engaging teeth

FIG. 15.4.—MAAG synchronous clutch coupling—relative positions of the teeth at successive stages of engagement.

16. COUPLINGS

Gear tooth couplings are widely used with double helical gearing because of their accuracy in tooth division and ease in assembly (Fig. 16.1). The external teeth can be slightly crowned in all directions to cater for an angular deviation of about 3 to 10 minutes (1 in 1000 to 3·3 in 1000) according to the speed. The floating

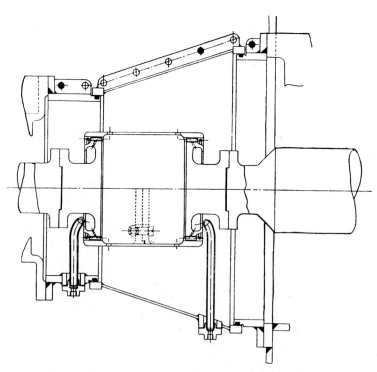

FIG. 16.1.—Pametrada Standard Flexible Coupling. No external flanges. Sleeve retained by circlip at each end. Small tooth pitch. Sleeve/claw EN 25/8 phosphated plus moly-disulphide. Ample free-flowing lubrication. Teeth barrelled. Good service results. (T. W. F. Brown, I.E. & S. 1960–61).

FIG. 16.2.—Gearing end of fine-tooth gear-type flexible coupling showing damage caused by misalignment. (Goodwin, *Naval Gearing Requirements*—Ref. 136).

FIG. 16.3.—Metastream coupling. (Beale and Gowans, I.Mar.E. Trans. Vol. 82, No. 7, p. 262).

member should be as light as possible, and dynamically balanced for high speed, and should have no radial play.

The material of the internal teeth could be quenched and tempered high tensile CrNi steel, or a nitrided steel, while the external teeth could be surface hardened and ground with some degree of crowning. These give good service when straight-aligned.

Various other methods of improving the performance under misaligned conditions are used, viz. the use of molybdenum disulphide, and phosphate treatment.

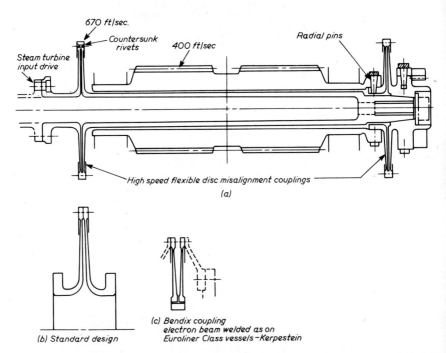

FIG. 16.4.—Thin disc diaphram coupling. (Metropolitan Vickers 1930, Wolff Proc. I.Mech.E. 1951 and Ljungstrom 1922).

All types have lubricating arrangements to the teeth, radial holes at each tooth space, flooded and free flowing to remove sludge and detritus. When under torque and misaligned with axial movement or vibration, large friction forces at the teeth arise which can be mildly troublesome or catastrophic. Young [135b] showed how bending moments due to misalignment arise as the loaded inclined teeth move axially into the position of maximum load. If fretting begins, the surfaces are likely to deteriorate rapidly with misalignment and axial movement against the high frictional loads.

Such was the case, described by Goodwin,[136] in a frigate with fine tooth couplings having barrelled, crowned and nitrided teeth (Fig. 16.2). The misalignment was 1 in 860 with axial vibration.

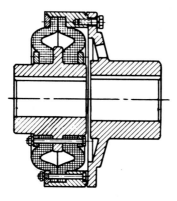

FIG. 16.5.—Vulcan rubber flexible coupling.

This and other experiences have led to the use of flexible couplings of the membrane type or the thin, steel-disc types. These have been tested at the G.E.C. laboratories, at Trafford Park, under torque and combined angular misalignment.[101] Metastream membrane type couplings (Fig. 16.3) are used in the County and Tribal Class vessels. Figs. 6.1 and 6.7 show the torque range possible with the Turboflex type of membrane coupling.

The thin steel disc type of coupling, under full load torque at high speed, withstood a misalignment of 1 in 180 for 10×10^6 cycles, with no sign of distress.

In fact, this type has been used for many years. Fig. 16.4a shows an example in a turbo-locomotive built in the early 1930s.[142] They were also a feature of the early Metropolitan-Vickers aero and land gas turbines, G.E.C.(U.K.)—Fig. 16.4b.

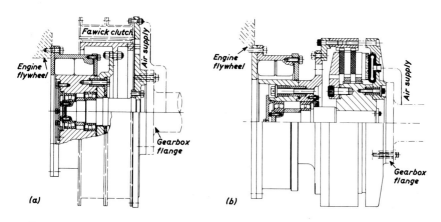

FIG. 16.6a.—Holset Fawick clutch-coupling combination with support bearing assembly.

FIG. 16.6b.—Holset/Wichita clutch-coupling with support bearing assembly.

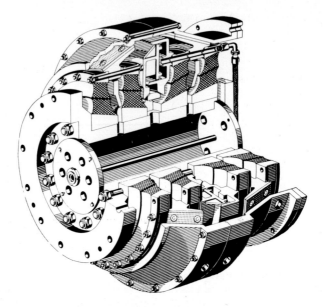

Fig. 16.7.—Pneumaflex—highly elastic clutch-coupling. (Lohmann and Stolterfoht A.G. Witten—Federal Republic Germany. 1972).

It is interesting to note that they have appeared again in another form on the Euroliner Class vessels built by De Schelde and in gas turbine destroyers.

With the advent of electron-beam welding, the manufacture of the thin discs has been simplified permitting variation in the design. Fig. 16.4c gives a sketch of the 22-inch o.d. diaphragm coupling of Bendix manufacture as used in the Euroliner Class vessels.

A 64-inch o.d. Bendix diaphragm coupling has been used by Westinghouse Marine Division, U.S.A., in a full scale back-to-back gear test, transmitting 15×10^6 lb inch torque at 120 rev/min.[138]

Alternatives to this are the membrane types and, for heavy duty, the Bibby spring, Renk sleeve spring, Holset and Vickers rubber block and Turboflex laminated couplings.

For diesel drive, the fluid coupling was almost universal in earlier days, but the slip loss was a disadvantage. This has now been overcome by the addition of an inverted SSS clutch, which is not required when manoeuvring, but is automatically clutched in for direct drive. The associated couplings would be much smaller, as they would only be required for starting and manoeuvring.[132]

The Vulcan rubber type coupling (Fig. 16.5) is an alternative, as already described in section 9, and can accept large powers.

Oil wetted clutches are common for lower powers and pneumatic aircooled types of either drum, or multiplate, are popular for higher powers.

Several clutch-coupling combination types are available e.g. Figs. 16.6 and 16.7. The rapid increase in power presents greater problems in clutch development.

17. LUBRICATING OIL SYSTEMS

The lubricating oil system is a most important part of gearing installations, its duty being to supply the correct quantity of oil to the bearings and gear meshes, at the correct pressure and temperature, with a minimum of aeration and water content, and a very high degree of cleanliness. Safeguards must be included in the event of failure.

The system is usually a combination of direct pressure and gravity supply. Usually, oil is supplied by two electrically-driven pumps, one on stand-by, with a third driven direct from the gearing. All pumps operate in parallel.

The pumps also supply oil to the overhead tanks at a height of about 30 ft (9 m) from where it can flow under gravity to the gearbox components and back to the drain tank.

Should both electrically-driven pumps fail, the pressure falls in the lubricating oil system and activates a trip system, closing the manoeuvring valve. As the engine runs down, oil will be supplied from the gravity feed tanks and from the direct driven pump during which time the emergency oil pump can be started. Rimmer [130] points out that, to maintain the flow rate at low speeds, the capacity of the direct driven oil pump will be determined by the oil requirement at part speed. This means that, at the higher speeds, surplus oil will be by-passed through the relief valve to the drain tank.

Discharge through the relief valve greatly increases the aeration in the tank. This can be overcome by replacing the direct driven pump by a hydraulic pump which powers a variable displacement hydraulic motor. This in turn drives an oil pump mounted on the drain tank beside the electrically driven pumps. This hydrostatic drive can incorporate suitable control arrangements, so that the lubricating pump provides the desired oil quantity over a large part of the power range.

Fig. 17.1 shows this scheme as used by Stal Laval [131] for their two-plane and multi-plane gearing.

Other basic components, in lubricating oil systems, are the drain tank, coolers, filters, centrifuges and vents.

Drain tanks should have a capacity of about three to seven times the quantity of oil circulated per minute, known as three to seven minutes' residence time. The smaller the capacity, the greater will be the amount of air at the pump suction. To reduce the aeration the design of tank shown in Fig. 17.2 is recommended. [105]

123

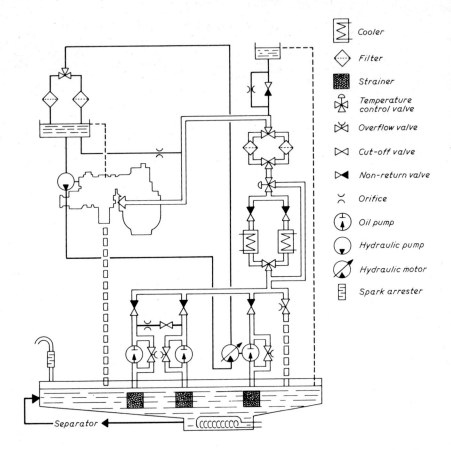

Cooler

Filter

Strainer

Temperature
control valve

Overflow valve

Cut-off valve

Non-return valve

Orifice

Oil pump

Hydraulic pump

Hydraulic motor

Spark arrester

FIG. 17.1.—Lubricating oil system for two-plane and multi-plane gearing. (Stal-Laval).

FILTERS AND CENTRIFUGES

The standard of filtration must be related to the minimum oil film thickness in the bearings and on the gear teeth; these are of the order of 12 to 30 microns and 1 to 5 microns respectively.

Clearly it is not practical to use filters of this capability, so, in addition, a lubricating oil centrifuge could be used to remove the hard particles which are below the range of a good filter. Centrifuges can remove hard particles as small as 1 micron. Rimmer[130] suggests a combination of full flow filters passing 10% of 30 micron particles, operating in conjunction with a by-pass centrifuge dealing continuously with about 20% of the oil, or a very much higher filter efficiency with a reflux cleaning system.

VENTS

Tests have shown that the ambient pressure in the gearbox can be marginally sub-atmospheric in certain places, and is invariably lower than the pressure in the drain tank. A large amount of water is removed from the oil by evaporation in the drain tank, when it is properly vented. Care has to be taken with vents that they do not promote the ingress of moist air to the system.

In general, the design temperature at inlet at full power is 120°F (50°C) with a temperature rise of 30°F (16°C). The rate of oxidation of oil increases with temperature and the maximum bulk temperature should not exceed 170°F (77°C).

In very high speed bearings, the oil temperature can be very much higher in the oil film, e.g. 240°F, which in the catchment area at the bearing outlet reads 170°F. However, the amount of oil involved at these high temperatures is a small proportion of the total, so the influence of the local high temperature does not have a serious effect on the oil.

The design pressure in the oil manifolds should be about 10 lb/in², but, with epicyclic gears, it should be about 20 lb/in², to account for the centrifugally generated back-pressure.

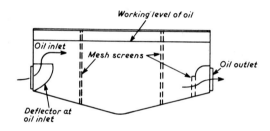

FIG. 17.2.—Scheme for oil drain-tank giving good de-aeration. (Rimmer).

Orifices are usually fitted in the pipes from the manifold, to ensure that the required oil quantity and pressure is maintained at each bearing inlet. Care has to be taken that there is always a positive pressure after the orifice, at the actual entry to the bearing.

If valves are used instead of orifices for ease of adjustment, they must be of the type which cannot be entirely shut off.

The oil drain should be very large to allow both oil and vapour to be discharged. The equivalent pipe diameter on a " half-full " basis would be $d = \sqrt{gpm}$ inches.

FLUSHING

Great care must be taken during manufacture and assembly of the gearbox to ensure cleanliness. After welding is completed and the swarf removed, the box is stress-relieved, wire brushed and pickled, followed by phosphating to remove mill scale and rust, and the surfaces wetted by an oil film. After machining and recleaning, assembly of the components can take place.

Various methods have been tried to protect the internal surfaces, but with the use of EP oils, the oil itself is sufficient to prevent corrosion.

Flushing of the oil lubrication system is very important and it is usually carried out by using the motor driven pump at maximum speed, circulating the normal service oil at temperatures between 70° and 80°C. By using isolating valves, various branches of the system can be flushed separately.

The centrifuge should run continuously during flushing. Special micro-filters of 40 to 50μ inch are used. Flushing may take as long as 48 hours.

18. ADJUSTABLE BEARING HOUSINGS

One of the main problems, in marine main propulsion gearboxes, is to ensure that the bearing housings are bored with sufficient accuracy. This problem was accentuated in the COSAG, Y102A gearing which had 58 journal bearings to accommodate the prime movers and reversing gears (Fig. 4.3—Y102).

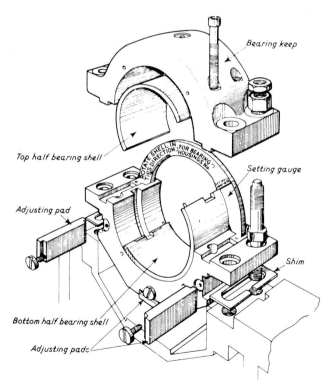

Fig. 18.1a.—Typical bearing housing showing shell and setting gauge. Y102. G.E.C.(U.K.).
(Weaving and Sampson, I.Mar.E. Trans. Vol. 75).

Separate bearing housings were designed so that their positions could be adjusted by packing pieces. These were so successful that they have been adopted as general practice in all main propulsion units of G.E.C.(U.K.)— Fig. 18.1a and 18.1b.

The housings are positioned with precision and can be adjusted to suit the gear bedding where necessary. Because the housings are comparatively small and separate from the gearbox, they may be machined with greater precision and the bores may be honed, thus permitting the use of medium wall bearings. The gear case seat for these bearing housings are thus flat landings and side supports which only require simple machining.

Adjustable bearing housings of this design have several advantages over conventional bored bearing housings, in manufacture, precision in setting both on test and in service.

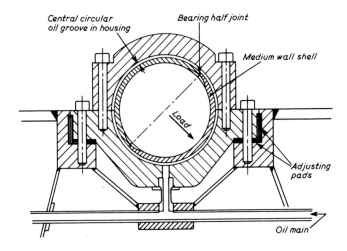

FIG. 18.1b.—Typical adjustable bearing designed to take shock loads as required, simplifies the machining of the gear case and alignment of the pinion.

With thin and medium wall bearings with $t/d = 1/50$ and $1/30$ respectively, the peripheral length of the liner exceeds that of the housing bore. Thus when it is inserted and clamped down between the bearing keep and the housing by strong bolts, an interference fit is provided between the liner and the housing. This prevents movement of the sleeve when in operation.

The oil supply groove in the housing and keep runs round the back of the liner and supplies two diametrically opposite oil inlet holes and oil distribution grooves at the liner joints, the latter subtending an angle of about 30°. The radial setting of the liner joint can, therefore, be set to give the best arc between the oil inlet and the load line. Thermocouples are located as near as possible to the position of minimum oil film thickness and are imbedded in small white metal plugs held in contact with the bearing shell. Such bearings have become standard.[122]

In the early development of these bearings, thin wall liners were tried, but it was found that if vibration occurred in the running line the thin liners could be battered into the oil supply groove. Medium wall thickness liners were sufficiently robust to withstand such treatment.

Cleanliness is again important. A particle of grit, trapped between the back of the bearing and the housing into which it is fitted, can produce a heavily loaded spot on the bearing surface and could cause a bearing failure. This is especially so with thin walled shells.

It is advisable to have chamfers at the oil distribution grooves at the oil inlets. Their use is twofold: one is to flush out abrasive particles which tend to collect in the bearing, and the other is to reduce the oil outlet and whitemetal temperature at the expense of a greater oil flow.

It is also necessary, in determining bearing clearances, to allow for tolerance on manufacture and wear in service, both of which would be about $0 \cdot 001$ inch/inch for the above 7-inch diameter bearing.

If the position of the load in the bearing varies under different operating conditions, the oil inlet should be placed at a position greater than $30°$ ahead of the nearest load-line position.

19. BEARING CHARACTERISTICS

It is necessary to appreciate the behaviour of journal bearings. Osborne Reynolds, in 1886, was the first to evolve the theory of lubrication for bearings of infinite axial width. Accurate analyses have been obtained for bearings of finite width.[119] A simple theory for the very narrow bearing has been given by Ocvirk,[120] 1952, which is satisfactory for bearings with a L/D ratio less than 1, and is helpful in understanding the problems. The Ocvirk " short bearing approximation " gives importance to the axial pressure gradient and neglects the circumferential.

When a lubricated journal rotates, it rises from the bottom of the shell and takes up an eccentric position, as in Fig. 19.1a, forming a convergence between the shaft and the bearing, compressing the oil dragged into that region and developing pressures to support the external load. As the bearing is of finite width, the pressure distribution is parabolic across the width, but rises to a peak in the central circumferential direction, as shown, falling off to zero slightly beyond the point of minimum clearance.

Beyond this point, the oil film develops no pressure and, at most, a little air or vapour is sucked in at the edges, and in that respect a second pressurised oil supply to that region, as in gear bearings, is beneficial.

The important parameter in the Ocvirk theory representing these actions is the capacity number C_n, or operating condition, given by:

$$\frac{ZN}{P} \left(\frac{D}{C_d}\right)^2 \left(\frac{L}{D}\right)^2 \text{ and is a function of } n \text{ as shown in Fig. 19.1b.}$$

Z = the mean operating viscosity within the loaded interspace [121]
N = the shaft speed, rev/min
P = load intensity lb/in² of projected area
D = diameter of journal   (R = shaft radius)
C_d = diametric clearance   (C_r = radial clearance)
L = width of bearing
n = the eccentricity of the journal.

The eccentricity, n, is involved in all other factors such as minimum oil film thickness, journal attitude $\varnothing$, pressure distribution and peak pressure position α, friction, horsepower loss and oil flow through the loaded region. The latter three determine the temperature of the bearing which for high speed bearings can be a limiting factor. Fig. 19.2 shows typical isotherms in running bearings

130

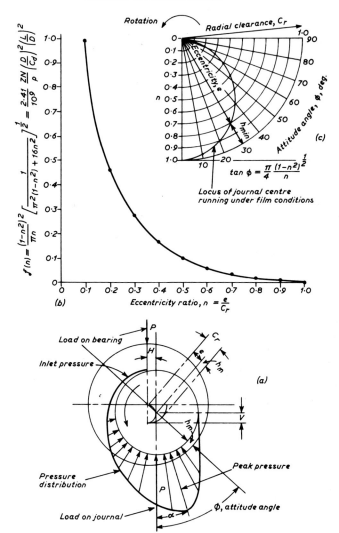

FIG. 19.1a.—Journal bearing—eccentricity, film thickness and attitude angle under operating conditions.

FIG. 19.1b.—Relationship between the capacity number—or operating condition—and the eccentricity ration.

FIG. 19.1c.—Locus of journal centre under running conditions giving eccentricity, film thickness and attitude angle.

measured by thermistors [123] on a test rig and Fig. 19.3 the temperature as measured by thermocouples on a shore trials set.

The oil supply to the bearing consists of the hydrodynamic flow in the loaded region of the bearing and the supply pressure oil which includes leakage through the chamfers at the ends of the distribution grooves. Thus:

oil supply $= Q_C + Q_{SL} +$ supply pressure flow, where Q_C is the circumferential

flow at the end of the pressure film $= \dfrac{ULC_r (1 - n)}{2}$

Q_{SL} is the side leakage which from Cole [125] is approximately $ULC_r \, n \left(1 - 0 \cdot 25 \dfrac{L}{D}\right)$

Hence the oil supply is:

$$Q_S = \frac{ULC_r}{2} \left(1 + n - 0 \cdot 5 \, n \frac{L}{D}\right) + \text{supply pressure flow.}$$

Fig. 19.4a shows these two flows.

Fig. 19.4b shows the effect of increased supply pressure and bearing clearance on the oil flow. An increase in clearance increases the flow and reduces the temperature, but does not alter the minimum oil film thickness very much, as this is determined by the pressures in the converging film supporting the same external load. Neither is there much change in the power loss, because the operating viscosity increases with the increase in cooling oil flow due to increase in clearance. The expression for power loss is $HP = 2\pi^3 (DN)^2 (DL) \dfrac{Z}{C} j$, where j is a function of the eccentricity n,[121] which increases rapidly from unity for $n > 0 \cdot 7$.

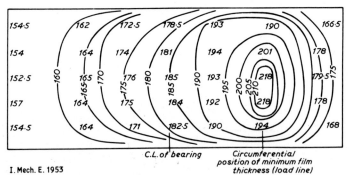

I. Mech. E. 1953

FIG. 19.2.—Typical Isotherms in Running Bearings.
Full journal bearing, Admiralty white metal on bronze; diameter 6 inches; length 4 inches; diametral clearance 0·012 inch; journal speed 185 ft per sec, journal load 500 lb per sq in on projected area; lubricating oil OM-88; oil inlet temperature 120° F, oil inlet pressure 5 lb per sq in; oil flow to bearing 3 gall per min. Temperatures in deg. F measured in white metal. (I.Mech.E. conference on Steam Turbine Research and Development 1953—Paper by T. W. F. Brown).

TEMPERATURE

Overheating of the whitemetal is the usual cause of wiping or bearing failure. Rig tests on bearings show that the local failure temperature of the whitemetal on steel is about 340 to 350°F.

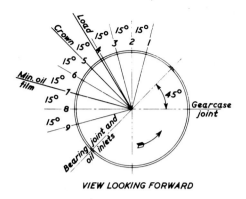

VIEW LOOKING FORWARD

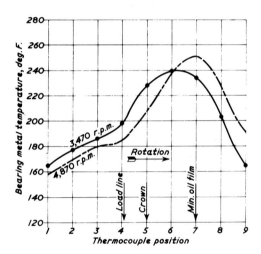

FIG. 19.3.—High speed bearing temperature—shore trials. 7″ × 4″ − 0·0022 inch/inch dia. clearance. 170°F oil temperature at outlet. (G.E.C.(U.K.) Y102). (Weaving, I.Mar.E. Trans. Vol. 75).

The 7 in × 4 in bearing shown on Fig. 19.3 had a maximum temperature of 250°F while running with a peripheral velocity of 149 ft/s with a specific load of 208 lb/in² and a diametrical clearance of 0·00225 inch/inch. The corresponding oil outlet temperature was 168°F.

A further reduction in temperature can be made by guttering the joints at 45° to a depth of approximately 1/16 inch running axially from the oil inlets to the ends of the bearing. Fig. 19.5 shows the results of such tests. The optimum amount of guttering in this case was 1/16 inch and, with an oil inlet pressure of 8–10 lb/in², the whitemetal temperature was reduced 20°F approximately, with an increase in oil flow from 1·5 to 2·5 gal/min.

nment of the journal within the bearing had little influence on the
entre position on one series of tests, indicating that the rig did not exert
g couple on the misaligned journal, but this was inconclusive as it may
due to the flexibility of bearing supports. Nevertheless the eccentricity at
the ends of the journals can be greater than the mean.

Oil starvation can cause wiping and vibration. Although the remedy is obvious,
good watch-keeping of oil outlet temperatures is important.

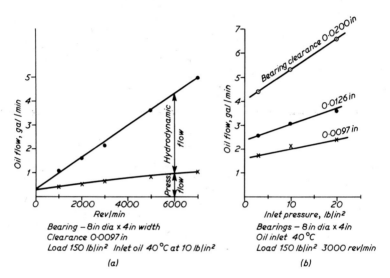

FIG. 19.4.—Oil flow in journal bearing—effect of speed, inlet pressure and clearance.
(Wilcox (109)).

BEARINGS AND VIBRATION

Bearings play an important part in determining the critical speeds of high
speed assemblies incorporating long quill shafts with flexible couplings and, also,
in the whirling speeds of the propeller and line shafting.

Two distinct types of vibration tend to arise:

(1) Vibration caused by imposed forces such as out-of-balance, misalignment
with gear tooth couplings, and out-of-round of journals. These are
damped by lubricated bearings and reduced in frequency from the simple
critical speed, by the flexibility of the oil film and the bearing supports.

(2) Self-excited vibration determined by the oil film properties, broadly known
as " half-speed whirl " or " oil-whip ". Various expedients are available
for dealing with oil whirl to which a lightly loaded, circular bearing is
prone. If this is liable to occur, a change in the type of bearing will be
required. In the extreme, three-land bearings could be used with the
two top lands as pressure loaded tilting pads.[126] These have been found
to have great stability.

Such problems have been investigated in depth by turbine engineers and have been explained by D. M. Smith [127] from a background of operating experience and correlated analysis.

In the calculation of critical speeds, unbalance forces are taken into account together with the flexibility and damping of the bearings. This gives the sensitivity of the vibrations in the response to a specified unbalance, by which the severity of the various criticals can be judged. [128]

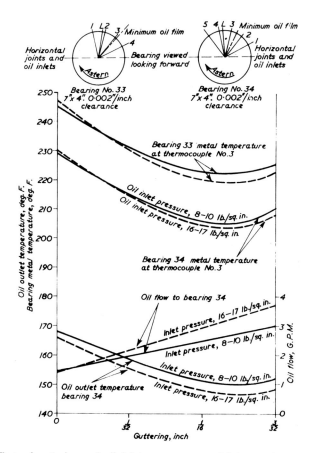

Fig. 19.5.—Effect of guttering and oil inlet pressure on metal temperatures and oil flow at 3500 hp/171 rev/min (Y102. G.E.C.(U.K.).

MAIN WHEEL BEARINGS

On the main wheel bearings of the COSAG–Y102 gears, various combinations of turbine gave rise to a range of load lines around the circumference. Some of these came close to the oil inlet, thus reducing the oil flow to the bearing, with a consequent increase in temperature. The design was changed to one with a central circular groove, with oil holes spaced around the diameter. The main wheel bearings as is usual had thick shells.

A circular groove splits the bearing into two, reducing the load capacity. However, there was ample margin at 345 lb/in² bearing pressure and 10 lb/in² inlet pressure throughout the full speed range.

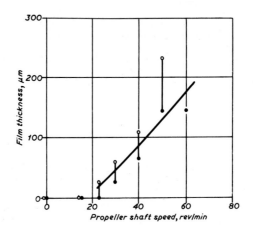

FIG. 19.6.—Minimum oil film thickness at end of stern tube bearing on a 200,000 dwt tanker. Upper and lower limits. (Jung and Larrson—SNAME 1972 (116)).

BARRING SPEEDS

Barring of the turbine is necessary to create blade ventilation to prevent the hot rotors from bending. Barring speeds over 30 rev/min would be desirable, but this would give quite a thrust with a large propeller. Speeds below 10 rev/min would certainly cause wear on the whitemetal of the propeller bearings, because of boundary friction, and possibly on the main bearings, if very large wheels are used. Fig. 19.6 shows the problem (Jung). Forced lubrication could be used on supertanker stern bearings as in Fig. 19.7.[67] Jung and Larsson offer an interesting alternative with an SKF roller bearing for the VLCC propeller stern tube bearing.[34]

Main thrust bearings are of the flooded tilting pad type and, ideally, the pads should be supported on a ring of pivoted balance arms, to ensure equal loads on each pad. The ahead and astern pads, at least, should be of the off-set pivoted type. Oil is pumped in at the bottom of the housing and circulated around the pads, leaving at the top. Journal bearings should not be incorporated in the housing.[56]

Troubles have occurred with whitemetal corrosion and wire wooling, especially with 3% Cr.Mo steel thrust collars. Hard particles become imbedded in the whitemetal and tear the surfaces. Agreement has not been reached as to the cause but with good filtration and the use of 1% Cr.Mo steel (EN19), the trouble has disappeared.

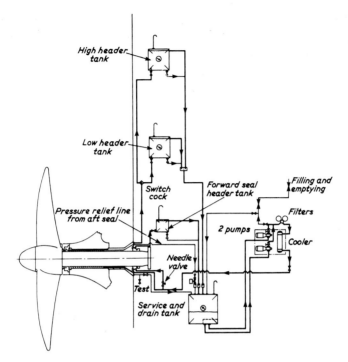

FIG. 19.7.—Stern bearing forced lubrication system. (Emerson, Sinclair, Milne—Million ton tanker. I.Mar.E. Trans. Vol. 83—1971).

High speed thrust bearings of the flooded tilting pad type used with single-helical gears are a source of relatively high loss. Successful efforts have been made to develop direct spray lubricated pads, which reduce the loss considerably.

Taper-land thrust bearings have been used at a specific pressure slightly less than that used on the tilting pad. This is the problem with high speed, single-helical gears unless the thrust is taken by the prime mover. The reliability of course is unimpaired.

SPRAYERS

A relatively small quantity of the oil supplied to the gear teeth is entrained between the tooth contacts, the remainder being necessary to remove the heat resulting from tooth friction and churning losses.

It is essential to keep the bulk temperature of the surface of the gears down to a minimum, as this controls the viscosity on which the thickness of the oil film between the tooth contacts is determined.[99] The total amount of oil required can be based on a tooth loss of 0·3 to 0·5% Ref (A) and a bulk oil temperature rise of 30°F, and assuming that all the heat generated in engagement of the gears is withdrawn by the oil sprayed on to them, giving a flow of 1·5 gal/min 1000hp per 30°F per mesh. Oil is sprayed through the jets, at a supply pressure giving sufficient jet velocity relative to the circumferential gear speeds to wet the gears effectively before being flung off. The spray nozzles must spread the oil across the face. Solid circular jets directed on to deflecting surfaces are preferred to slits, as these are liable to block. Various schemes are in use.

The position of the sprayers is important. Shell, Ref (D) point out that power losses and overheating in high speed gears may be reduced by applying some of the oil to the teeth as they disengage, this being on the side where the cooling effect is greatest. This has prevented scuffing and shows the importance of reducing the bulk temperature in this respect.

With helical gears, oil is displaced along the length of the teeth and, in the case of double-helical gears with apex leading, the oil is displaced outwards and in the opposite direction with the apex trailing. In the latter case the gap serves as an escape route.

20. KINEMATICS OF TOOTH MESHING—HERTZIAN CONTACTS, SURFACE FINISH AND OIL FILM GENERATION

It is necessary to understand the kinematics of tooth meshing, the effects of error in tooth form, the thermal effects and misalignment, the need for good surface finish and surface quality, good load distribution, and profile and longitudinal corrections.

The theoretical helical tooth is an involute helicoid, i.e. a screw surface formed by a sloping line, ab, on a sheet, abde, as it is unwound from the base cylinder (Fig. 20.1). This generating line is tangential to the base helix at all positions on the helicoid, and a plane can touch the involute helicoid along the generating line. Thus an involute helicoid can be finished ground by a flat sided abrasive wheel.

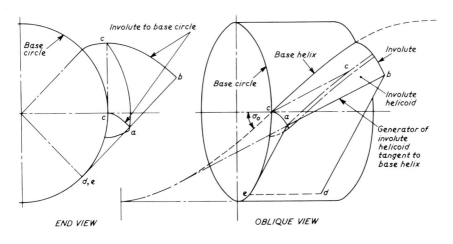

Fig. 20.1.—Development of Involute Helicoid.

Two involute helicoid mating teeth make contact along the generating line. This line in transverse section (Fig. 20.2) is called " the line of action " and is a tangent to the two base circles. Thus, at every point of contact, the common normal passes through the pitch point and the teeth profiles are said to be " conjugate ".

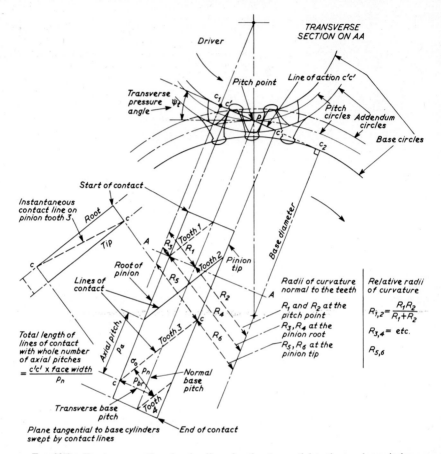

Fig. 20.2.—Transverse section showing line of action tangential to the two base circles.

Fig. 20.4.—Developed plane of surface of action, showing the contact lines on several helical teeth at the same time.

With increased centre distance, the mating teeth make contact as before, but on a different part of the involute and at a different pressure angle. This is one of the special features of involute teeth and is usually demonstrated by the " crossed belt " analogy (Fig. 20.3).

The developed plane of the " surface of action " shows the contact lines on several teeth in mesh at the same time. Fig. 20.4 shows how the load is taken up, first at the root of the leading end of the driving helix, and disengages at the corner diagonally opposite to that at which contact began. The oil which is not entrained between the contact is swept along at the axial velocity of the contact line and mixes with the hot oil which passes through the contact.

The contacting teeth roll without slip across the tooth face, but roll and slip up the face. The velocities of rolling and sliding up the face are shown in the transverse plane (Fig. 20.5), where it is seen that pure rolling takes place at the pitch point and sliding is greatest at the tips of the driving and driven wheels. To minimise the possibility of scuffing at the tips, the sliding velocities there are best made equal by an addendum modification during manufacture. This is achieved by displacing the cutter laterally outward from the blank which still generates involutes of the same base diameter, but giving different outside and root diameters and tooth contact at a different working part of the involute. This technique was first developed by MAAG, Ref (B).

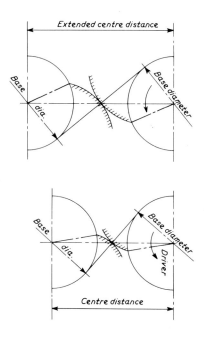

FIG. 20.3.—The crossed belt analogy.

The radii of curvature changes along the line of action, thereby changing the relative radius of curvature, R_r, as shown in Fig. 20.5. This changes the stress conditions of the contact lines along their length. The surface stress criterion is given by:

$$S_c = \frac{W_{IC}}{R_r}$$

where W_{IC} is the load per inch length, acting normal to the contact.

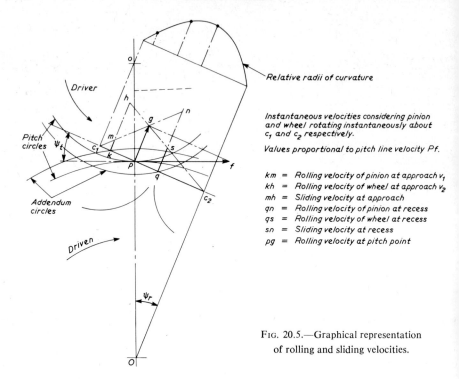

Driver

Pitch circles ψ_t

Addendum circles

Driven

ψ_r

Relative radii of curvature

Instantaneous velocities considering pinion
and wheel rotating instantaneously about
c_1 and c_2 respectively.

Values proportional to pitch line velocity Pf.

km	$=$	Rolling velocity of pinion at approach v_1
kh	$=$	Rolling velocity of wheel at approach v_2
mh	$=$	Sliding velocity at approach
qn	$=$	Rolling velocity of pinion at recess
qs	$=$	Rolling velocity of wheel at recess
sn	$=$	Sliding velocity at recess
pg	$=$	Rolling velocity at pitch point

FIG. 20.5.—Graphical representation
of rolling and sliding velocities.

From this, the maximum Hertzian compressive stress on the contact for a steel-steel combination is:

$$S_{max} = 2290 \sqrt{S_c} \text{ lb/in}^2$$

and the width of the flat caused by the compression at the contact is:

$$W = \frac{0 \cdot 56}{10^3} R_r \sqrt{S_c} \text{ inch}$$

Combining the compressive stresses, shown in Fig. 22.2, gives the maximum shear stress:

$$S_{\text{max shear}} = 0 \cdot 3 \, S_{max}$$

which occurs at a depth of $0 \cdot 39W$ beneath the surface.

The width of the flats can range, on various gears from $20/10^3$ to $100/10^3$ inch.

These moving contact flats, by virtue of their shape, generate an oil film between the teeth, the thickness of which is approximately:

$$h = 12 \cdot 0 \, (\eta_o \, [v_1 + v_2] \, R_r)^{0 \cdot 5} \quad . \quad . \quad . \quad 1$$

where

h is in micro-inches.

η_o is the viscosity in poises, at the temperature of the teeth.

$[v_1 + v_2]$ is the oil entrainment velocity in ft/sec.

R_r is the relative radius of curvature in inches.

The value of h for high speed gears would exceed 50μinch.

Once the oil is drawn into the pressure zone of the flat, its viscosity becomes so great that the oil separates the surfaces and supports the load. At approach and recess, the oil film is sheared by the sliding velocity thereby increasing its temperature and decreasing its viscosity to a certain extent in its passage through the contact. Attention was first drawn to the problem by Blok [97] who discussed the frictional traction of the interacting asperities generating sufficient heat to cause the local oil temperature to rise to the flash point; during the last 25 years great progress has been made in understanding the " elasto-hydrodynamic " problem.

The shape of the loaded surfaces was predicted by Russian workers.[98] Crook [99] measured the oil film thickness and the shape of the oil film between smooth

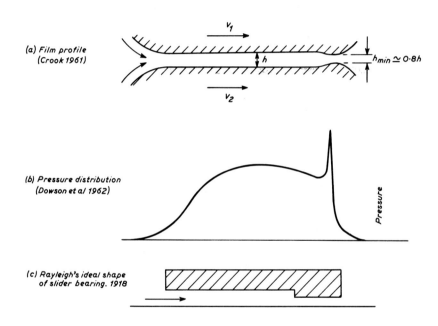

$$v_1$$

(a) Film profile
(Crook 1961)

$$h$$
$$h_{min} \simeq 0.8h$$

$$v_2$$

(b) Pressure distribution
(Dowson et al 1962)

Pressure

(c) Rayleigh's ideal shape
of slider bearing. 1918

Fig. 20.6.—Characteristics of loaded surfaces showing (a) the constricted exit and (b) the corresponding pressure distribution. (c) was suggested as the ideal shape for a slider bearing. (The lubrication of industrial gears—Shell International Petroleum Co. 1964).

discs and gear tooth contacts (Fig. 20.6) which has been confirmed by other workers.[100, 101] Dawson [107] showed the great influence of surface finish and how, where the film thickness was greater than three times the sum of the CLA values of the mating surface finishes, scuffing was unlikely to occur.

If the surface finish is poor, contacts between the asperities can be made through the almost rigid oil film, generating heat and causing the temperature of the gears to rise and the inlet viscosity to fall, resulting in a thinner oil film. This could result in incipient scuffing, mild wear and serious tearing. With materials such as EN (25/8) and the correct lubricant, incipient scuffing would polish out quickly. With hardened gears the smoothing out process takes longer. The risk is high during the running-in period, but can be minimised by the use of a chemically active EP oil, or with surface treatment such as phosphating or copper-plating on case-hardened gears, after which the risk is negligible.

21. INTRINSIC PROPERTIES OF OIL/MATERIAL COMBINATIONS

LUBRICANT AND SCUFFING

It is important to choose the correct lubricant to prevent scuffing. A straight mineral oil may suffice or, if conditions are severe, an extreme-pressure lubricant may be required.

Various methods are used for evaluating the oil-material combinations, such as the small back-to-back gear oil test rigs with $3\frac{1}{2}$ inch centres designed by the Institute of Automobile Engineers (I.A.E.), Fresslastgrenze von Zahngetrieben (F.Z.G.) and the Ryder (U.S.A.) and the Admiralty Oil Laboratory (A.O.L.), narrow faced disc machine.

These machines have narrow face-widths in order to get repeatability in the determination of the intrinsic properties of the oil/material combinations. The results from these, in conjunction with full scale back-to-back tests and service experience, give the background for the choice of the oil/material combination.

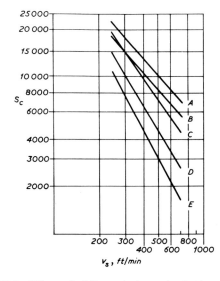

Lubricant temperature, 69–74°C
Approximate viscosity at 60°C
cSt A150, B110, C85, D50, E27

Slide/roll ratio

$$\left(1 - \frac{v_2}{v_1}\right) = 0.5$$

$$\left(1 - \frac{v_1}{v_2}\right) = -1.0$$

FIG. 21.1.—Effect of sliding velocity and oil viscosity on scuffing load with EN30B Discs. (H. J. Watson—" The Choice of Lubricants " I.Mech.E. 1958).

145

In general the scuffing load increases with the oil viscosity at the bulk temperature of the gears. It decreases with sliding velocity, $v_1 - v_2$, Fig. 21.1—Watson [103] and the curves are raised or lowered with a decrease or increase in the slide/roll ratio, $(v_1 - v_2)/v_2$, the rolling velocity v_2 being the lower surface speed [103]—Fig. 21.2.

Blok [97] showed how the temperature rise, brought about by the friction of asperity contacts, which added to the bulk temperature at the mesh, may reach the flash point of the oil, e.g.:

$$T_c = T_b + T_f$$

$$\text{where } T_f \simeq \frac{W_{1C}{}^{\frac{3}{4}}}{6 \text{ to } 8 \ R_r{}^{\frac{1}{4}}} (v_1{}^{\frac{1}{2}} - v_2{}^{\frac{1}{2}}) \quad . \quad . \quad . \quad 2$$

and T_c is the contact temperature °F

T_b is the bulk temperature

T_f is the increase in temperature to cause the flash

W_{1C} and R_r as before.

The factors 6 to 8 apply approximately to steel on steel.

Clearly it is important to keep the bulk temperature as low as possible by supplying the optimum amount of the correct oil, especially a portion to a point near the exit from the mesh, where the temperature is highest, giving the most effective cooling. The expression T_f applies to ideal conditions, as when obtaining the intrinsic properties. With actual gears of moderate face-width, possible mis-alignment and small deviations from perfection, the risk will be increased. From full scale tests and trials experienced on hardened gears, a factor of $3 \pm 1 \cdot 2$ would cover the few results available. The wide variation is typical of the problem. Reasonable design values are given by Wydler.[118]

While scuffing, welding and tearing is associated with the tips of the teeth, pitting, which includes abrasive wear and enfoliation, occurs on the dedendum just below the pitch line.

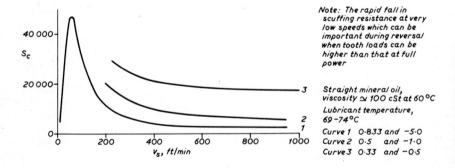

FIG. 21.2.—Effect of sliding velocity and slide/roll ratio on scuffing load with EN30B Discs. (H. J. Watson).

22. PITTING AND TOOTH BREAKAGE

Pitting is a surface fatigue phenomenon, starting from minute cracks initiated by asperity interaction, which first run approximately parallel to the surface at about 40 μinch beneath the surface. With repeated action, some of these open up to the surface and those on the dedenda are propagated by the hydraulic pressure of the oil trapped in the crack just before the Hertzian contact passes over it, when it is sealed by the rolling action.

The inner part of the crack extends and turns up to the surface and a flake of material falls away. The minute cavity is called a pit [108, 112]—Fig. 22.1a.

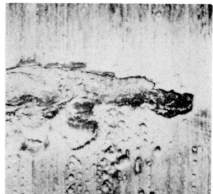

FIG. 22.1a.—Conchoidal in soft steels.   FIG. 22.1b.—Exfoliation and flaking in hard steels.

(W. T. Chesters—Study of the surface fatigue behaviour of gear materials.—Inter. Conf. on Gearing. I.Mech.E. 1958. Plate 9 21.2).

FIG. 22.1.—Examples of pitting.

The extended cracks on the driving teeth are inclined so that they go from the surface towards the pitch line and *vice versa* on the driven teeth. This is in accordance with the direction of the friction drag on the addenda and dedenda. Not all the authorities agree on the direction of the cracks on the addenda, where pitting rarely occurs, but all agree with their direction on the dedenda which permits the hydraulic action.

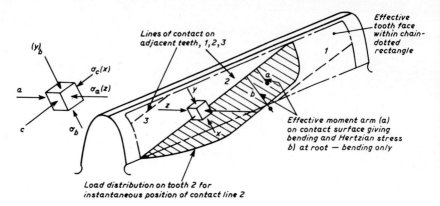

(a) Load distribution

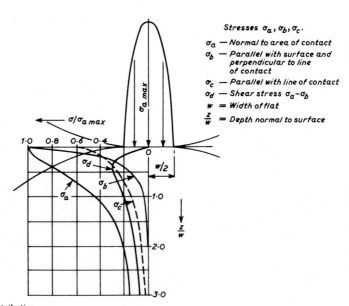

(b) Stress distribution

FIG. 22.2a.—Load distribution on tooth for instantaneous position of contact line.
FIG. 22.2b.—Hertzian stresses on contact line for a specified load.

Pitting is not a serious trouble if it is of the " pin-head " type, as this usually
ceases. Progressive pitting is a rare occurrence.

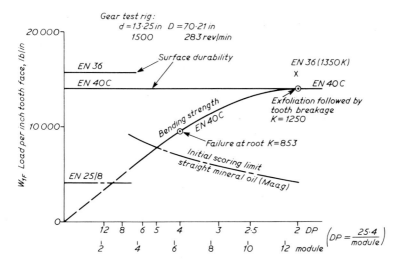

Fɪɢ. 22.3.—Results of full scale endurance tests on nitrided gears plotted as " load per inch tooth face " on a base of tooth pitch. No scuffing occurred with EP oil.

The flaking action on the dedenda of the pinion and wheel can take place simultaneously with through-hardened gears (soft-on-soft), causing wear which in time can settle down and give satisfactory service (see pp. 18, 153, 154, 155). The ultimate stress for pitting occurs when the maximum Hertzian pressure is about equal to the tensile strength of the material for both through-hardened and case-hardened surfaces.[112]

When the surfaces are very smooth, the onset of pitting is delayed and, when the oil film is substantially greater than the total roughness of the surfaces, pitting does not occur at all, even at a stress greater than at the pitting fatigue limit.[106, 107] The effect of oil film thickness is clearly shown by the increased resistance to pitting with speed on small scale experiments [106] and by the first reduction gears of the *Nestor-Neleus* and HM ships described (Refs 24 and 28).

23. EXAMPLES OF GEAR DAMAGE

TOOTH BREAKAGE

Pitting can occur on case-hardened gears under very high loading and it sometimes appears as enfoliation and flaking (Fig. 22.1b) and can lead to tooth breakage. Recent investigations show that the Hertzian compressive stresses should be considered in conjunction with the tensile bending stresses because of their phase relationship.

Consider a spur tooth of a driving pinion. The load comes on at the root and sweeps up to the tip. The material, at the various parts of the effective tooth force, first gets the Hertzian compressive stresses and then later the bending stresses. So, also, with a helical pinion, where the inclined contact line sweeps across the tooth face, the compressive stresses being followed later by the more complicated cantilever-plate bending stresses up the tooth (Fig. 22.2). The stresses at the root below the effective tooth face are not affected by the rolling contact.

The Hertzian stress concerned is the minor principal stress σ_b (Fig. 22.2), as this runs in the same direction as the stress due to bending. Both of these stresses tend to propagate cracks on the dedenda.

FIG. 23.1.—Scuffing due to partial block of an oil sprayer supply on a gas astern train. (I.Mar.E. Trans. Vol. 75, 1963. Y102 astern gear). Hand honing was sufficient to permit normal running.

FIG. 23.2.—Welding and tearing. (Frederick and Newman (139) plate 6—Fig. 13–3a. I.Mech.E. Conf. on Gearing 1958).

These two sets of stresses give a stress range of minus to plus of varying magnitude up the tooth face and in the tooth depth, instead of the zero to plus of simple bending, as occurs at the root and in pulsator tests.[143] This complicated system of stresses has been analysed by Mudd[50] taking into account the residual stresses of surface hardening and profile modifications. Attempts have been made to display the results on a Smith fatigue diagram together with the fatigue limits from the zero to plus pulsator tests, the reversed plus/minus bending of the Schenk tests and the surface fatigue limit zero to minus from the discs test, without success. Different dynamic effects occur in each method of testing and there are too few full scale test results. However, another method of plotting, introduced by Sigg,[41] includes all the effects discussed and " shows on one diagram the influence of the three criteria, i.e. bending fatigue strength, surface durability and oil film resistance ".

For particular gears for the required horsepower, speed reduction, centre distance, face width, pressure and helix angles, the load per inch face, W_{if}, is plotted on a base of tooth pitch for all three criteria as shown. Fig. 22.3 which shows the results of the 4dp and 2dp tests plotted on this basis. The 4dp set failed by bending at the root at a load of 9500 lb/inch face corresponding to a K value of 853, and a specific bending load W_{if}/P_n of 12 000 lb/inch per inch pitch.

DEVELOPMENT OF AN EDGE-TYPE DISC MACHINE

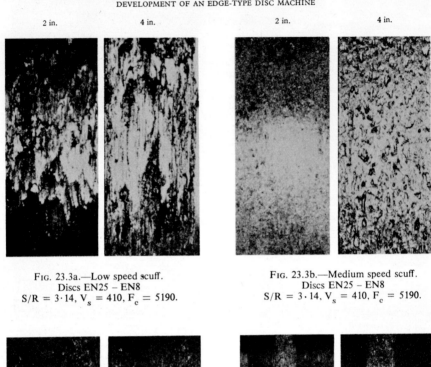

FIG. 23.3a.—Low speed scuff.
Discs EN25 – EN8
$S/R = 3 \cdot 14, V_s = 410, F_c = 5190.$

FIG. 23.3b.—Medium speed scuff.
Discs EN25 – EN8
$S/R = 3 \cdot 14, V_s = 410, F_c = 5190.$

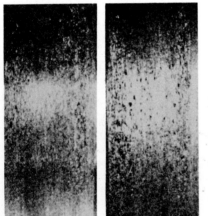

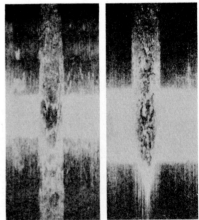

FIG. 23.3c.—High speed scuff.
Discs EN25 – EN8
$S/R = 3 \cdot 14, V_s = 410, F_c = 5190.$

FIG. 23.3d.—Initiation of scuff.
Discs EN25 – EN8
$S/R = 3 \cdot 14, V_s = 410, F_c = 5190.$

FIG. 23.3.—Results from narrow faced disc machine. (V. J. De Gruchy and P. W. Harrison—
A.O.L. Development of an edge type disc machine. I.Mech.E. 1963. Fig. 14.5).

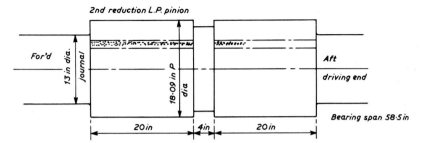

FIG. 23.4.—Pin-head pitting due to misalignment.

On the 2 dp pinion, there was exfoliation of the surface at about the pitch line which led to a fatigue crack and tooth breakage in that area. The load was 14 000 lb/inch face, corresponding to a K value of 1250 and a specific bending load of 8900 lb/inch per inch pitch. The ultimate surface load is influenced by surface cracking and bending stress and is taken as that, corresponding to the maximum K value of 1250. The core strength in the region is increased to 67

FIG. 23.5.—Wear on dedenda—Stabilised wear on second reduction gear. (W. H. Darlington, Ref. 24).

tons/in² by strain hardening which extends to 55/10³ inch as shown by tests on nitrided discs (Dawson).

The bending fatigue limit values would curve as shown, especially towards the area where the bending stress approaches the core strength, showing the more severe influences of surface stress on the bending fatigue stress at that point. No scuffing occurred. This is due in part to the step-by-step increase in loading, the great resistance to scuffing of nitrided gears, the good surface finish, 10 to 20 μ-inch, and the oil film thickness at the tips of the teeth of approximately 75 μ-inch. An EP oil was used. These results for nitrided gears are in the order of magnitude as for carburised case-hardened and ground gears.

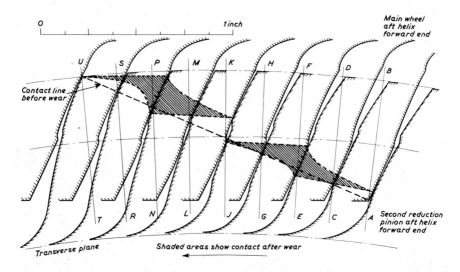

Fig. 23.6.—Section through the teeth referred to in Fig. 23.5.

For comparison the best of the results from the full scale gear trials on through-hardened gears [44] is shown for the combination EN (25/8) which gave, for 0·6 dp, a failure bending load of 3850 lb/inch corresponding to a K value of 486 and a specific bending load W_{if}/P_n of 6420. Slight pitting occurred at 425K, 3350 lb/inch at the pitch line, but it was not progressive. No scuffing occurred, showing the merit of this excellent material combination. The oil used was a straight mineral oil, OM.100. However, the tremendous difference between soft-on-soft gears and hard-on-hard is apparent. Finally, gear damage in all its forms is accentuated by misalignment which when observed should be corrected.

Examples of various types of failure are shown below:

Scuffing:
   in service   Fig. 23.1
   scuffed discs   Fig. 23.3a, b, c and d
Welding and Tearing;   Fig. 23.2
Pitting: Fig. 23.4
                             Fig. 22.1a and b

Tooth Breakage:

Fig. 23.7
Fig. 23.8
Fig. 23.9
see also references 23 and 25

Wear:

Fig. 23.5
Fig. 23.6

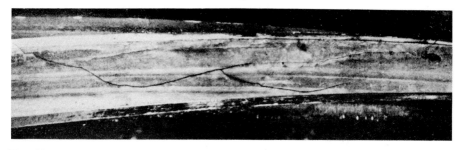

FIG. 23.7.—Path of crack in hardened and shaved pinion tooth (" Back to back testing of marine reduction gears ", A. Cameron and A. D. Newman. Conf. on Steam Turbine Research and Development. I.Mech.E. March 1953. Plate 5, Fig. 91 (d)).

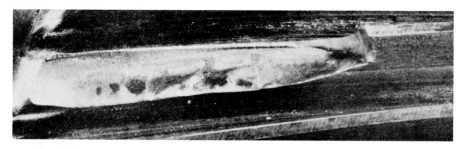

FIG. 23.8.—Broken tooth on same pinion as tooth in Fig. 23.7 exhibiting fatigue failure.

WEAR STEPS ON THE TWO DEDENDA

Fig. 23.5 illustrates wear steps on the two dedenda which, in this instance, stabilised and ran quietly and efficiently for years.[24] This is a typical type of the wear with soft-on-soft, low speed gears. The centre portions of the shaded areas correspond closely to two circular arcs, the unworn convex addenda and the worn concave dedenda, equally displaced before and after the pitch point, and below and above the pitch line.

This is somewhat similar to the combined form of conformal Novikoff teeth.[147 to 151] Conformal circular arc gearing, in its simpler form, gives a thicker oil film and a relatively higher load than involute gearing, because of its larger relative radius of curvature, as occurs, for example, with the planet and annulus contact in epicyclic gearing. Conformal gearing has progressed in industry and in very highly loaded light gears for aero-engines,[151] where the involute gear has reached its limit. Such gears will not be discussed in this review, but what must be referred to is the fact that highly accurate, involute teeth of through-hardened material, with good surface finish, operating at low speed, can wear smoothly on the dedenda to conform to the approximate circular arcs of the addenda, then stabilise and work smoothly and quietly.

If the profile of the addenda and surface finish had been poor, the wear would not have stabilised. Hence it is still most essential to have accurate gears to allow the phenomenon to take place.

With hard-on-soft gearing with good surface finish, the dedendum of the case-hardened gear does not wear, and so conjugate wear does not occur. The dedendum of the through-hardened gear polishes and thus gives an increase in load capacity.

FIG. 23.9.—Tooth failure influenced by heavy pitting. (S. H. Frederick and A. D. Newman, " Gear Failure " p. 77—Fig. 13.4, Plate 7. Conf. on Gearing. I.Mech.E. 1958).

24. GEAR NOISE

GENERATION OF NOISE

Gear noise is due to vibrations caused by impacts and non-uniform angular velocities of the rotating gears, arising from pitch errors and inaccuracies in tooth profile, shocks on entering and leaving the mesh, errors due to the deflection of the teeth and pinion under load. Secondary causes are eccentricity, unbalance, rolling and sliding friction at the contacting surfaces. Tip and root relief on the profile and longitudinal corrections are important means of reducing the magnitude of these impacts.

When there is an opening in the gearcase, sound radiation comes direct from the vibrating gears and, when the case is closed, it impinges on the walls and panels of the gearcase, which vibrate and transmit it with some modification to the surrounding atmosphere. The sound also comes through the shafting and the oil films at the bearings.

As a result, the gearcase vibrates at all the forced vibration frequencies and harmonics due to the errors and at all the impulse-excited natural frequencies of the whole system. Flat panels of low damping on the gearcase make good sound radiators, as does the upper structure of the engine room and the double bottom on which the gearcase is seated.

Errors in pitch and profile can have numerous frequencies. If the profile error is repeated on every tooth the predominant note may correspond to the frequency of tooth engagement, i.e. contact frequency = number of teeth of wheel or pinion times their corresponding rev/sec.

Other causes of noise are:

(1) irregular pitch errors may produce a variety of noises according to the speed of the gears and the resonant properties of the gears and casing;

(2) eccentricity and cumulative pitch and short span errors give noise at rotational frequency and multiples of it;

(3) errors in surface finish give a continuous spectrum which could be important if there is resonance with structural parts;

(4) hobbed helical gears in earlier days produced a note corresponding to the number of teeth on the worm wheel drive of the hobbing machine table times the rev/sec of the wheel.

Combinations of these can give sum and difference frequencies of the contact frequencies. Any of these vibrations and resultant radiator tones may be accentuated by coinciding with a natural frequency of the gear element or case. A minute amount of energy can create considerable noise. To control or suppress

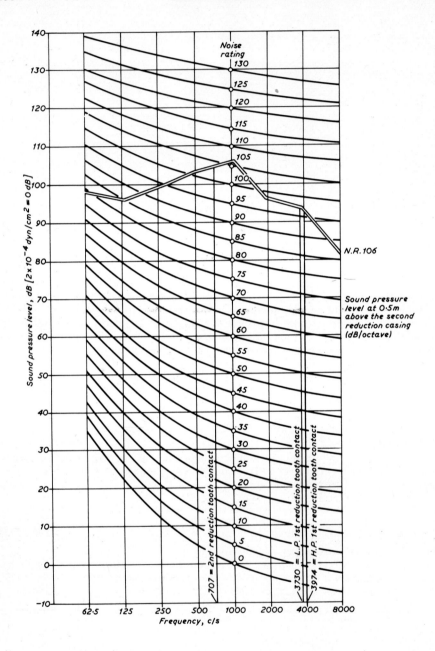

Fig. 24.1.—Noise Spectrum for High Power Turbine Gear.

it requires great skill. New methods of recording and analysing gear errors, and their resultant noise spectra are being developed.[157]

The superb accuracy in gear manufacture, tooth correction and surface finish has about reached the physical limit of improvement that can be made on the source of the noise. Noise is characterised by the total sound pressure level (S.P.L.), measured in decibels (dB) with the reference pressure 20 μ N/m² = 0·0002 dynes/cm² as a datum level.

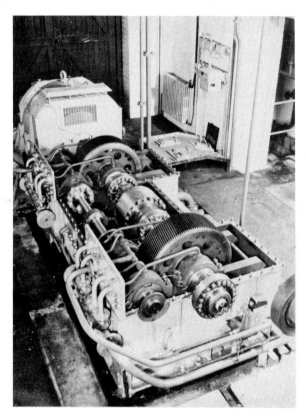

FIG. 24.2.—Back-to-back gear test rig at G.E.C. (A.E.I.) used for a wide range of investigations covering many aspects of gear design and the evaluation of various combinations of gear steels. The effects of temperature, speed, load, alignment, tooth accuracy and surface finish can be studied in connection with the noise level.

To get a complete picture, the information is given in the form of a sound spectrum in frequency bands of one octave, or half-an-octave or less, expressed as S.P.L. in dB per octave or per half-an-octave etc, specifying the position of the microphone relative to the source of the noise. Similarly the associated vibration measurements, usually taken with an accelerometer placed on the gearbox, are expressed in dB, the reference vibration velocity being 4·6 × 10⁻⁸ m/s. Thus the

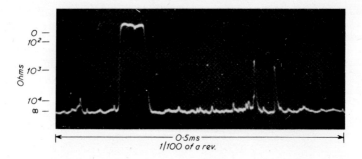

FIG. 24.3.—The variation of oil film resistance due to asperity contacts as shown on an oscilloscope. The resistance of the oil film itself is very high so that the resistance values measured give an indication of the amount of metallic contact, which is dependent upon both the roughness of the surfaces and the thickness of the oil film. (G.E.C.(U.K.)).

character and magnitude of the vibration and noise can be determined. Rogue resonances with gear panels, etc, can possibly be removed by stiffening or damping. Fig. 24.1 shows a noise spectrum for turbine gears.

REDUCTION OF NOISE

Systematic studies that have been made with varying helical gear parameters such as helix angles, pressure angle, overlap and diametral pitch, did not show any consistent substantial cure for gear noise. As noted before, spur and helical gears can have longitudinal corrections to suit the bending and twisting of the pinion body for one particular load.

Profile corrections to spur teeth can give a smooth transition between the one and two pairs of teeth carrying that particular load. Helical gears require an integral number of axial pitches and correct helices to achieve smooth running and, as these are easier to produce than profile correction, helical gears have a much better chance of quiet running than spur gears.

Failures occurred in the early development of the aero-gas turbine propeller drives when spur gearing was used, due to the much higher speeds than those used on piston engine propeller drives. Helical gears were subsequently used with success.

Surface effects on test gears, using resistance measurements of the oil film between the contacting surfaces, illustrate the behaviour of sequential cycles of endurance running, shutting down and starting up again, and helped to discern the noise from this source (Figs. 24.2, 3 and 4).

Palliatives such as rubber between the wheel and the rim showed, in one test, that it was no quieter than a normal wheel. It would appear that it would be necessary to have both radial and circumferential resilience between the pinion and its shaft as well to get much effect. Damping the gear panels, which may tend to vibrate, with a layer of proprietary damping material on the outside and other means can effect reductions of 5 to 7 dB.

However, the only way of achieving substantial reduction of gear noise is by enclosing the gear in a suitable acoustic hood, and preventing the escape of noise

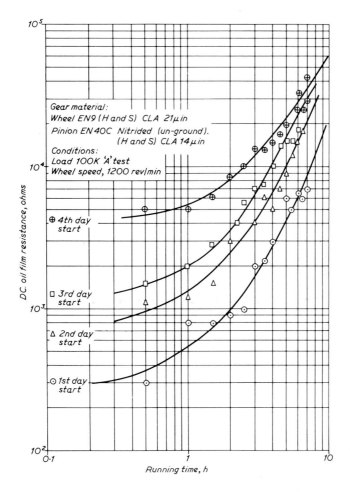

Fig. 24.4.—Back-to-back gear test rig. Resistance/time measurements for 4 consecutive days running. (G.E.C.(U.K.)).

by properly designed resilient mountings under the gear, and at the input and output flexible couplings.[154]

The Constant-Position-Mounting System (CPMS) is used for the reduction of noise and vibration, and the retention of alignment.

The Constant-Position-Mounting System is an active mounting system which has been developed by Y-ARD.[136] A section of one of the units is shown in Fig. 24.5. Several of these are used, some to act vertically, reducing vertical movement between the base of the ship and the gearbox, and some horizontally, installed between the sides of the ship and the gearbox, thus reducing sway. The mounts can be arranged to control in all degrees of freedom. The principal parts are:

(1) two air chambers;
(2) an orifice damper;
(3) an integral feed-back servomechanism.

It operates as follows. When the gearbox descends relative to its design position, the air is compressed and acts as a spring, the flow of air through the orifice effecting damping. Meanwhile the valve comes into play and supplies oil at a rate proportional to relative displacement of the gearbox and the base, thus varying the mounting pressure to apply a position correcting force to the gearbox.

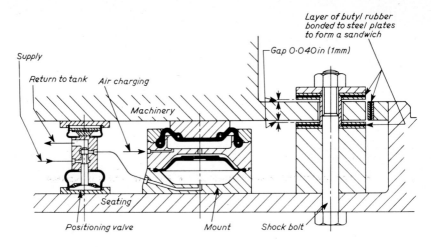

Fig. 24.5.—Diagrammatic section through CPM positioning valve, mounting and shock stop. (Y. ARD).

The control system has great sensitivity and can deal with rolling and pitching frequencies. It restricts at 20° roll to about ±0·02 inch (± 0·5 mm) which is much better than conventionally mounted systems. At higher frequencies, the attenuation approaches that of the ideal system. Thus, the CPMS is particularly suitable for mounting gearcases where large misalignments would be intolerable. It also greatly reduces the transmissibility of the gear tooth noise through the ship to the sea. Shock bolts with rubber bonded plates are included, limiting the maximum movement to ± 0·04 inch (1 mm).

Lutje-Schipholt suggests possible alternatives to this scheme, using rubber pad mountings for noise and cardan shaft connections, with flexible couplings having good misalignment capabilities [158]—Fig. 24.6.

The raft mounting, shown in Figs. 7.30 and 3.71b for the DDH.280 machinery and associated Vulcan nylon-rubber coupling, shows the tremendous effort made to suppress noise, even with very accurate gear machinery.

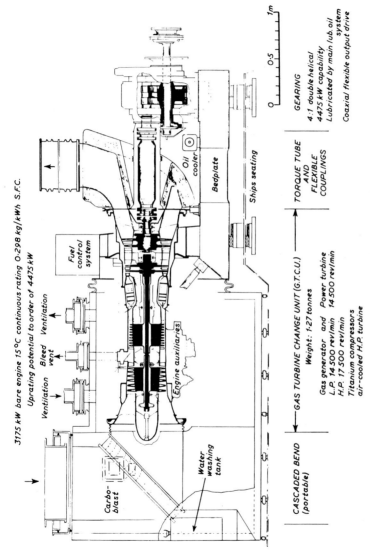

3175 kW bare engine 15°C continuous rating 0·298 kg/kWh S.F.C.

Uprating potential to order of 4475 kW

Ventilation   Bleed   Ventilation
              vent

Carbo-
blast

Water
washing
tank

Engine auxiliaries

Fuel
control
system

Oil
cooler

Bedplate

Ships seating

CASCADED BEND (portable)	GAS TURBINE CHANGE UNIT (G.T.C.U.)	TORQUE TUBE AND FLEXIBLE COUPLINGS	GEARING

Weight: 1·27 tonnes

Gas generator and   Power turbine
L.P. 14 500 rev/min   14 500 rev/min
H.P. 17 500 rev/min
Titanium compressors
air-cooled H.P. turbine

4:1 double helical
4475 kW capability
Lubricated by main lub oil
                    system
Coaxial flexible output drive

FIG. 24.6.—Free power turbine Tyne propulsion module. (R. M. Lutje—Schipholt, I.Mar.E. Trans. 1975. Vol. 87).

25. REFERENCES

A. Merritt H. E., *Gears*. Pitman, London.
B. *MAAG Gear Book*. 1963.
C. Tuplin, W. A., *Gear Load Capacity*. Pitman. 1962.
D. Shell International Petroleum Co. *Lubrication of Industrial Gears*. 1964.

HISTORY AND DEVELOPMENT OF GEAR-HOBBING MACHINES
1. Jung, Ingvar. G. de Laval Memorial Lecture 1968. *The High Speeds and the Gear*—reviews early development of accurate hobbing machines and the split ring index wheel by de Laval Co. U.S.A. 1904–11.
2. Davis, A. W. C. A. Parsons Memorial Lecture, *Trans.I.Mar.E*. 1974—reviews the marine turbine industry and the influence of the gearing problem.
3. Parsons, Sir Charles A. " Mechanical Gearing for the Propulsion of Ships ". *Trans.I.N.A*. 1913—explains the cause of singing in gears and introduces the creep process in hobbing.
4. Tomlinson, G. A. " The Accuracy of Large Hob-Cut Helical Gears ". *Engineering*. 1928. Vol. 125, p. 405.
5. Meldahl, A. " Why does a Gear Sing?", *Brown-Boveri Review*. 1942—A classic description of the cause and cure.
6. Couling, S. H. " The Production of High Speed Helical Gears ". *Proc.I. Mech. E*. 1943.
7. Sykes, A. " Progress in Turbine Gear Manufacture ". *Proc.I.Mech.E*. 1947.
8. Timms, C. " Measurement of Errors in Turbine Gears ". *Proc.I.Mech.E*. 1947.
9. Newton, J. M. " On the Accuracy of Gear-Hobbing Machine Tables ". *Proc.I.Mech.E*. 1948.
10. Tuplin, W. A. " Developments in Marine Reduction Gearing ". *Trans.I. Mar.E*. 1948—discusses overlapping effects of hob cuts.
Tuplin, W. A. " Forms of Tooth Surfaces in Creep Cut Helical Gears ", *Engineering*. London. 1951. Vol. 2, p. 484.
11. Braddyll, J. R. G. " Large Gear Hobbing Machine and Post-Hobbing Processes ". Inter.Conf. on Gearing, *Proc.I.Mech.E*. 1958. Paper 9.
12. Martinaglia, L. " Developments on Gear Grinding Machines ". Inter. Conf. on Gearing, *Proc.I.Mech.E*. 1958. Paper 35.
13. Hadcroft, A. " Precision in Marine-Gear Manufacture: A Modern Approach ". " Gearing in 1970 ", *Proc.I.Mech.E.*, Vol. 184, Pt. 30, p. 153—shows how hobbing and grinding machines can be corrected to the limits required.

TOOTH LOADING

14. Lewis, F. M. " Load Distribution of Reduction Gears—a Graphical Analysis ". *Trans.A.S.M.E.* 1945.

15. Weber, C. and Banachek, K. *Load Distribution on Gear Teeth.* D.S.I.R. Sponsored Research 15. 1950. Munich.

16. Davis, A. W. " Marine Reduction Gearing—Pinion Distortion and Misalignment Modified by Tooth Deflection ", 28th Thomas Lowe Gray lecture, *Proc.I.Mech.E.* 1956.

17. Shannon, J. F. *The Relationship between Lloyd's K Factor and the Ratio of Face-Width to the Diameter of Pinions.* A.E.I. Engineering Report 1962 and 5th Round Table Conf. on Marine Gearing. 1963.

18. Peraud, M. P. *Load Distribution along a Double-Helical Pinion.* 5th R.T.C. on Marine Gearing. 1963.

19. Sigg, H. " Profile and Longitudinal Corrections on Involute Gears ", *A.G.M.A.* 1965. Also 4th R.T.C. on Marine Gearing. 1961.

20. Walker, H. " Gear Tooth Deflection and Profile Modification ", *Engineer.* 1938, pp. 186, 409 and 494.
Walker, H. " Trends in Gearing ", *Engineer.* 1949. March 18.

21. Gregory, R. W., Harris, S. L. and Munro, R. G. " Dynamic Behaviour of Spur Gears ", *Proc.I.Mech.E.* 1963–64, pp. 178 and 207—gives optimum tooth correction at one particular load.

22. Kerpestein, J. B. " Computerisation of Gearing Design ", 8th R.T.C. on Marine Gearing. 1972.

MATERIAL COMBINATIONS

23. Joughin, J. H. " Naval Gearing—War Experience and Present Development ". *Proc.I.Mech.E.* 1951. Vol. 164, p. 157.

24. Darlington, W. H. " Some Considerations of Wear in Marine Gearing ". *Trans.I.Mar.E.* 1951. Vol. 68, p. 289.

25. Archer S. " Some Teething Troubles in Post War Reduction Gears ". *Trans. I.Mar.E.* 1951. Vol. 68, p. 309.

26. Dunlop, I. M. and Good, E. B. " Machinery Installations of Guided Missile Destroyers and General Purpose Frigates ". *Trans.I.Mar.E.* 1963.

27. Weaving, P. D. V. and Sampson, W. H. " Progress and Development in Naval Propulsion Gears. 1946–1962 ". *Trans.I.Mar.E.* 1963.

28. Gowans, B. J. McD. and Porter, F. E. " Naval Service Experience With Surface Hardened Gears ". *Proc.I.Mech.E.* 1970. Gearing in 1970.

29. Beale, G. B. and Gowans, B. J. McD. " Transmission Design for Warships of the Royal Navy ". *Trans.I.Mar.E.* 1970. Vol. 82–3.

30. Shannon, J. F. and Young, I. T. " Marine Turbine Propulsion Gearing 1960–1970 ". *Proc.I.Mech.E.* 1970.

31. Mott, I. K. " A Survey of Gas Turbine Transmission Components M.E.R." *Trans.I.Mar.E.* February 1972, p. 14.

32. Wahl, C. G. " Marine Gears, Present Position and Future Development ", *Brown Boveri Review.* Baden No. 8. August 1959—Brown Boveri thrust collar with single helical gears—Final reduction nitrided gears.

33. Steele, T. W. *Modern Marine Gears—Operating Experiences with the M.S.T. 14. Units.* G.E.(U.S.). 8th R.T.C. on Marine Gearing. 1972.

34. Jung, I. and Larsson, P. E. " Marine Turbine Gearing ". *S.N.A.M.E.* 1972. Stal-Laval.

35. MAAG—*The Standard MAAG Dual Tandem Articulated Marine Gears.* 1970.

36. Young, I. T. and Charles, C. J. " Evolution of a New Range of Marine Turbine Gear Boxes "—I.M.A.S. 1973. *Trans.I.Mar.E.*

37. Takeda, Y. " Development of a Japanese Design of Marine Steam Turbine Plant. Pitting and scuffing limits from service experience on through hardened gears ". *Trans.I.Mar.E.* November 1969.

38. Newman, A. D. " Load carrying tests on Admiralty gearing ". Inter. Conf. on Gearing. *Proc.I.Mech. E.* 1958. Paper 10.

39. Page, H. H. " Advances in Loading of Main Propulsion Gears ". Inter. Conf. on Gearing. *Proc.I.Mech.E.* 1958. Paper 12.

40. Chamberlain, A. " Development in the Heat Treatment of Large Marine Gears ". Inter. Conf. on Gearing. 1958 *Proc.I.Mech.E.* Paper 18.

41. Sigg, H. " Influence of Hardened and Ground Gears on System Design ". University Seminar Wisconsin, Milwaukee. 1965—Single-helical gear requirements.

42. G.E.C.(U.K.). " Bedding trials on single-helical gears (Y102) ". Internal report—confirms non-appearance of the tilting effect with single-helical gears with the precautions taken.

43. G.E.C.(U.K.). " Endurance tests with case-hardened pinions on through-hardened wheel rims 1965 ". Internal report.

44. Darling, R. F., Isherwood, T. and Ginty, A. G. " Full Scale Gear Trials on Through-Hardened Gears ". *B.S.R.A.* NS 65. 1964.

45. Niemann, G. *The Pitting Fatigue Strength of Gears.* Munich. 1962—gives tests with " hard on soft " materials.

TOOTH LOADING—RELIABILITY

46. Goodwin, A. J. H. *Review of the Rules for the Loading on Marine Gears.* 7th R.T.C. on Marine Gears. 1969.

47. Thoma, F. A. " An Updated Approach to Marine Gear Tooth Bending Strength ". *ASNME*, 1972. (Basic unit load $= W_{if}.dp$ (Dudley; $\dfrac{W_{if}}{P_n}$ (Goodwin)).

48. Harrison, W. H. and Mudd, G. C. " Proposal For a New World-Wide Gear Rating Procedure ". *B.G.M.A.* 1973.

49. Toms, A. E. " Some Factors in Marine Gearing for Classification Purposes ". *Trans.I.Mar.E.* 1975.

50. Mudd, G. C. " A Numerical Means of Predicting the Fatigue Performance of Nitride-Hardened Gears ". " Gearing in 1970 ". *Proc.I.Mech.E.* 1970. Paper 12.

51. Carter, A. D. S. " Achieving quality and reliability " (The reliability of a system with rough loading is that of the weakest link and not just the product of the reliability of each component, and by suitably coupling the various systems the reliability of each is not impaired). James Clayton Lecture 1974. *Proc. I.Mech.E.*

52. Jones, T. P. " Design, Operating Experience and Development Potential of Main Propulsion Epicyclic Gears ". *Trans.I.Mar.E.* 1972. Vol. 84, p. 450.

34. Jung, I. and Larsson, P. E. *loc. cit.* " Marine Turbine Gearing ". (52 and 34 give examples where suitable coupling of the various systems was required and ensuring adequate safety margins in tooth stress.)

53. Pugsley, A. G. *Repeated Loading on Structures*—Conference on the fatigue of metals, Melbourne. 1946. Paper 33.—The first paper on " scrambled " loading.
54. Meek, M. " Operating Experiences of Large Container Ships ". *Trans. I.E.S.* 1975—Measurements of the " scrambled " loads.
55. Andersen, H. C. and Zrodowski, J. J. " Co-ordinated Alignment of Line Shaft, Propulsion Gear and Turbines ". *Trans.I.Mar.E.* 1960. Vol. 74–4.
56. Volcy, G. C. " Damage to Main Gearing Related to Shafting Alignment ". *I.M.A.S.* 1969.
57. Carr, J. and Martyn, D. K. " Design Aspects of Propeller Shafting ". *I.M.A.S.* 1969.
58. Young, I. T. *Main Turbine Gearing—Sensitivity to Main Shafting Alignment.* 8th Inter.R.T.C. on Marine Reduction Gearing 1972.
59. Bunyan, T. W. *A Shipowners Approach to some Shafting Machinery and Hull Problems.* Europort Tech. Cong. November 1971—introduces the " Transflex " Wheel.
60. Young, I. T. *Main Shaft Laminated Flexible Coupling—a Solution.* Discussion on T. W. Bunyan's paper.
61. Verity, C. H. *Vickers Main Shaft Laminated Rubber Coupling—a Solution.* Discussion on K. M. B. Donald's paper—Marine Steam Turbine—*Trans.I.Mar.E.* 1972.
36. Young, I. T. and Charles, C. J. *loc cit.* (36)—(Turbine—gear—laminated flexible coupling). *I.M.A.S.* 1973.
62. Jakobson, A. M. and Langballe, M. *Structural interaction between ships-bottom-structure and reduction gears.* Royal Norwegian Council for Science and Industrial Research, 1971—Strain measurement on gear teeth in service.
63. Pinnekamp, W. " Performance of marine reduction gears ". *Trans.I.Mar.E.* 1975.—Strain measurements on gear teeth in service.
41. Sigg, H. *loc. cit.* (41)—(destroyer turbine-gear-condenser power package with 3 point support).
64. Norton, E. " Development in Naval propulsion ". Thomas Lowe Gray Lecture. *Proc.I.Mech.E.* 1973.

GEARING CONFIGURATION
65. Kemper, G. A. *Contradictory Trends in Marine Turbine Gearing.* 6th Inter. R.T.C. on Marine Gearing 1967.
66. Kerpestein, J. B. " Gear Transmission in the Euroliner Class Vessels ". *M.E.R.* April 1973.
67. Emerson, A., Sinclair, L. and Milne, P. A. " Million Ton Tanker ". *Trans. I.Mar.E.* Vol. 83, 1971. Milne, P. A. and Craig, M. F. " Future Developments in Machinery Installations ". *Trans.I.Mar.E.* 1975—limiting possibilities of marine propellers.
68. Jung, I. K. E. (Stal-Laval) " Steam Turbine Machinery ". *Trans.I.Mar.E.* 1969. Vol. 81–5—gives various propeller arrangements. *Primary and Secondary Epicyclic and Contra-Rotating Propeller Drives.* 6th Inter.R.T.C. on Marine Gearing 1967.
69. Michel, F. (AEG) " Contra-rotating Propellers with Interlocked Drives ". *Jahrbuch der S.T.G.* 1966. Springer, Berlin.
70. G.E.C.(U.K.) *Contra-rotating Propellers with Locked Train Interlocked Drives.* 1966 and R.T.C. on Marine Gearing 1967.

EPICYCLIC GEARING

71. Jones, T. P. and Allen, W. H. " Fifteen Years Development on High Power Epicyclic Gears ". *Trans.I.Mar.E.* 1967. Vol. 79–8. " Design, operating experience and development potential of main propulsion epicyclic gears ". *Trans.I.Mar.E.* Vol. 84–15, 1972.

72. Shannon, G. " An Allen Triple-Reduction Epicyclic Main Propulsion Gear Train for a G.E.(U.S.A.) Heavy Duty Gas Turbine ". *A.P. Engineering.* March 1976, No. 21.

73. Zink, H. (Renk) " Load Sharing, Smooth Running and Design of Modern Planetary Gearing ". *Konstruktion* 1964. Vol. 16—describes flexible annulus, supported by sleeve-spring packs, which permit radial, tangential and tilting moments and provides damping.

74. Stozle, K. (Renk) *Experience with High Power Planetary Marine Gears.* 8th Inter.R.T.C. on Marine Gearing 1972.

41. Sigg, H. *Influence of Hardened and Ground Gears on System Designs* (MAAG). 1965 Seminar on Systems analysis in gear design. Univ. Wisconsin, Milwaukee. *loc. cit.* (41).

75. Martinaglia, L. " Epicyclic Gearing for High Speed and High Torque Applications ". *B.G.M.A.* 1969. MAAG—Noteworthy paper on high speeds, thermal effects and tooth correction—low speed with high torque epicyclic gears using spur teeth.

76. Martinaglia, L. *Heavy Duty Planetary Gears for Marine Drives.* 7th R.T.C. on Marine Gearing 1969.

77. Sigg, H. " The use of Coarse Pitches in Marine Propulsion Gearing ". 8th R.T.C. on Marine Gearing 1972. MAAG.

78. Hicks, R. T. (Vickers) " Experience with Compact Orbital Gears in Service ". *Proc.I.Mech.E.* 1970. Paper 11—flexible pin type epicyclic gear.

79. Brown, W. M. (Vickers) " Epicyclic gears for Medium-Speed Diesel Engines ". *Proc.I.Mech.E.* 1970–4—flexible pin type epicyclic gears.

29. Beale, G. B. and Gowans, B. J. McD. " Transmission Design for Warships of the Royal Navy ". *Trans.I.Mar.E.* 1970. Vol. 82–7.—Discussion by W. M. Brown on parallel-planetary gear arrangements.

80. Coats, R. " Pametrada Standard Turbines. Present Position and Future Outlook ". *Trans.I.Mar.E.* 1965. Vol. 77/10.—Paraplan gearing.

30. Shannon, J. F. and Young, I. T. *loc. cit.* (30). " Marine Turbine Propulsion Gearing 1960–70 ". *Proc.I.Mech.E.* 1970.—Final reduction epicyclic gearing.

81. Biezeno and Grammel, R. *Engineering Dynamics.* Vol. II. Blackie 1956.— Toroidal deformation of rings—p. 213.

REVERSING

82. Goodwin, A. J. H., Irvine, J. H. and Forrest, J. " The Practical Application of Computers in Marine Engineering ". *Trans.I.Mar.E.* Vol. 80–7. 1968 (Y.ARD) —Ship manoeuvring and reversing with discussion.

83. Conn, J. F. C. " Backing of Propellers ". *Trans.I.E.S.* Vol. 78–2. 1934.

84. Gold, P. D. " Stopping and Backing Trials of a Destroyer ". *Jr.Amer.Soc. Naval Engineers.* Vol. 53.—Discussion by D. C. MacMillan, pp. 559–575—assimilated data on the stopping trials of about 20 merchant vessels.

85. Adley, A. A. and Lea, K. E. " Selection, application and installation of medium speed marine machinery systems ". *Trans.I.Mar.E.* 1968.—Reversing with Diesel Engines.

86. Brauer, H. (Renk) " Gearing Arrangements to Meet the Changing Requirements for Marine Propulsion ". *Jahrbuch der STG 1966*. Springer—reversing with diesel engines; isolating clutch and flexible coupling arrangements; oil immersed multiplate disc clutches for reversing, supplemented by shaft brake if required.

87. Young, I. T. *The Beneficial Role of Marine Gearing*. Liverpool symposium on marine propulsion systems 1974.—Reviews gear drives for a wide range of prime movers and their ancillary plant. Pneumatic aircooled clutches in combination with rubber couplings used for large power diesel engine drives.

88. Richardson, W. S. *A Reversing Gear for Large Vessels*. 6th Inter.R.T.C. 1967.—Development of the Falk-Airflex clutch; also ASME–67–GT.31.

89. Shannon, J. F. *The Development of a High Power Marine Reversing Gear*. 6th Inter.R.T.C. 1967.—Small hydraulic couplings, with increased oil throughput GEC–Y102 development with Fluidrive Co.

90. SSS Gears. *Twin-input Gas Turbine Hydraulic Coupling Reversing Gear*. 1976.

91. Clements, H. A. *SSS Gears*.—Operational experience of the SSS (Synchroself-shifting) clutch particularly in Naval Propulsion Machinery. *A.S.M.E.* 72–GT–81—gives SSS clutch conditions during reversing.

26. Dunlop, J. B. and Good, E. B. *loc. cit.*—discussion gives reversing conditions with hydraulic couplings.

27. Weaving, P. D. V. and Sampson, W. H. *loc. cit.*—discussion gives reversing conditions with hydraulic couplings.

92. Allen, H. G. N. and Jones, T. P. " The Application of High Powered Epicyclic Gearing for Industrial and Marine use ". *B.G.M.A.* 1960.—Reverse-reduction epicyclic gear box for H.M.S. Border-3500 shp.

93. Yates, D. E. " Epicyclic Gearing for Gas Turbine Main Propulsion ". *A.S.M.E.–76–GT–24.*—11,000 kW reverse-reduction epicyclic gear box with external braking.

94. Clarke, D., Patterson, D. R. and Wooderson, R. K. " Manoeuvring Trials with the 193,000 tonne dw Tanker ' Esso Bernicia ' ". *B.S.R.A. Rep.* NS295. 1970.—Rudder cycling tests.

95. Sperry Co. " The Sperry Steering Control System in use with Twin-Rudder Braking. MER. I ". *Trans.I.Mar.E.* 1975.

96. Roberts, J. B. " An Advanced High Speed Dynamometer for Testing Aircraft Tyres and Brakes ". *Proc.I.Mech.E.* 1974, Vol. 188.—Dunlop Co. test equipment with 120×10^6 ft.lb brake energy capacity.

ELASTOHYDRODYNAMICS
97. Blok, H. General discussion on lubrication. *Proc.I.Mech.E.* 1937. " Lubrication as a Gear Design Factor ". Inter. Conf. *Proc.I.Mech.E.* 1957. Paper 33—Scuffing.

98. Grubin, A. N. 1949; Petrusevich, A. I. 1951. Russian—English translation D.S.I.R.—Analysis predicting shape of oil film between teeth.

99. Crook, A. W. " Lubrication of Rollers ". *Phil.Tran.Roy.Soc.* 1958.—Measured shape of oil film.

100. MacConochie, I. O. and Cameron, A. 1958. *A.S.M.E.*

101. Dowson, D. and Higginson, G. R. 1960. *Proc.I.Mech.E.* 1970.

102. Meldahl, A. " The Brown-Boveri Testing Apparatus for Gear Material." *Engineering*, July 1939.—Test cylinders, loaded against each other, driven by

eccentric involute gear wheels, give the rolling and sliding conditions of gear tooth operation.

103. Watson, H. J. "Choice of Lubricants". Inter. C. on Gearing. *Proc. I. Mech.E.* 1958.—Scuffing.

104. Shotter, B. N. "Influence of Surface Finish on Gear Tooth Performance". Inter. C. on Gearing. *Proc.I.Mech.E.* 1958.—Experiments on discs.

105. Jacobson, M. A. I. "Crossed-Helical Gears". *Proc.Auto.Div.I.Mech.E.* 1961–62/1—gives range of surface finishes obtained by various methods of production.

106. Timms, C. "Recent Developments in Spur and Helical Gears". *Inst. Prod.Engs.—Engineering*, 8 April 1960.—Beneficial effect of improved surface finish and increased speed on the loading of gears with reference to pitting.

107. Dawson, P. H. "The Effect of Metallic Contact on the Pitting of Lubricated Rolling Surfaces. *Jr.Mech.Engr.Sciences* 1962—4.16.

108. Dawson, P. H. "Rolling Contact Fatigue Crack Initiation, by Asperity Interactions on a 0·3% Carbon Steel". *Proc.I.Mech.E.* 1968–69. Vol. 183–1.4.—Crack initiation and direction of flow.

45. Niemann, *The Pitting Fatigue Strength of Gears, and Ways of Improving It.* Munich 1962—Tests with "hard on soft materials"—*loc. cit.*

109. Niemann, G. and Rettig, H. "Lubrication Problems Associated with Gear Wheels". *Maschinenschaden* (1965)—Tooth surface damage; incipient surface cracks and their direction; Smith fatigue diagram combining Hertzian and surface friction stresses.

110. Crook, A. W. "Simulated Gear-Tooth Contacts". *Proc.I.Mech.E.* 1957. Vol. 171–5.—discussion by L. E. Benson on direction of metal flow on tooth surfaces.

111. Cameron, A. and Newman, A. D. "Back-to-Back Testing of Marine Reduction Gears". Conf. on Steam turb. research and development. *Proc. I. Mech. E.* 1953, pp. 32–33.—direction of surface cracks.

112. Chesters, W. T. *Study of the Surface Fatigue Behaviour of Gear Materials.* Inter. C. on Gearing 1958 (discussion by R. J. Love on incipient surface cracks and their direction from M.I.R.A. tests).

113. Shell. *The Lubrication of Industrial Gears.* 1964. Shell International Petroleum Co. London.—Directions of cracks, pitting and scuffing, pp. 125–230.

114. Merritt, H. E. "Gear Tooth Contact Phenomenon". *Proc.I.Mech.E.* 1962. Vol. 176/7.—a classical re-appraisal.

SCUFFING
115. Fowle, T. I. and Hughes, A. "Experience with EP Turbine Oils". *Proc. I.Mech.E.* 1970.

116. De Gruchy, V. J. and Harrison, P. W. "Development of an Edge-Type Disc Machine". *Proc.I.Mech.E.* 1962.—investigates intrinsic properties of gear material—lubricant combinations.

117. Dowson, D. "The Role of Lubrication in Gear Design". *Proc.I.Mech.E.* Gearing in 1970. Paper No. 9.

118. Wydler, R. "A method of Assessing the Danger of Scuffing". *MAAG Gear Book* and 4th Inter.R.T.C. on Marine Gearing 1961.

97. Blok, H. *loc. cit.*

103. Watson, H. J. *loc. cit.*

114. Merritt, H. E. *loc. cit.*
107. Dawson, P. H. *loc cit.*

BEARINGS

119. Cameron, A. and Wood, W.L. " The Full Journal Bearing " *Proc.I. Mech.E.* 1949. Vol. 161.—Applied Mechanics.

120. Ocvirk, F. W. " The Short Bearing Approximation for Plain Journal Bearings. *N.A.C.A. Tech.Note.* 2808–9. October 1952; Dubois, G. B. and Ocvirk, F.W. " The Short Bearing Approximation " *A.S.M.E.* Paper 54. Lub. 5. 1954.

121. Wilcox, D. F. and Rosenblatt, M. " Oil Flow, Key Factor in Sleeve Bearing Performance ". *A.S.M.E.* No. 51–A–89. 1951.

122. Glacier Metals Co. Ltd. *Thin and Medium Shell Bearings.*

123. Brown, T. W. F. " The Application of Research to Marine Turbine Development—Fig. 97—Typical Isotherms in Running Bearings ". Conference on Steam Turbine Research and Development. *Proc.I.Mech.E.* 1953.

124. Newman, A. D. " Bearings for Marine Geared Turbines ". *N.E.C.Inst.* 1956.—This and other work established the short bearing.

125. Coles, J. A. and Hughes, C. J. " Oil Flow and Film Extent in Complete Journal Bearings ". *Proc.I.Mech.E.* 1956. Vol. 70/17.

126. Shannon, J. F., Crook, A. W. and Duffin, S. (A.E.I.) *Turbine Generator Engineering A.W.C.*, p. 183.—Three-land bearings with two top lands as pressure loaded tilting pads. These have great stability and eliminate " oil-whirl " vibration.

127. Smith, D. M. *Journal Bearings in Turbo-Machinery.* Chapman and Hall 1969—dynamic characteristics, operating experience and correlated analysis.

128. Crook, A. W. " Vibrations Associated with the Running Line ". *A.E.I. Turbine—Generator Engineering* 1968.—The sensitivity of the vibrations in response to a specified unbalance can be predicted.

34. Jung, Ingvar and Larsson, Per-Erik. *Loc. cit.* " Marine Turbine Gearing ". *S.N.A.M.E.* 1972.—At low barring speeds, need for special type roller bearing with heavy propellers.

67. Emerson, Sinclair-Milne. *Million Ton Tanker. Loc. cit.*—Barring at low speeds—use of jacking oil.

129. Rann, F. E. and Simpson, W. A. Joint I.Mar.E. and MOD Navy Symposium on lubrication—Successes and failures.—Operating experiences with bearings in warship main propulsion systems.—Barring tests on journal bearings.

LUBRICATING OIL SYSTEMS

130. Rimmer, R. F. and Liddell, R. E. " Design of Lubricating Oil Systems for Marine Propulsion Gears ". *Trans.I.Mar.E.* 1969 and *Proc.I.Mech.E.* 1970. Paper No. 5.

131. Stal-Laval. *Advanced Propulsion Systems—Lubricating Oil Systems.*

CLUTCHES

132. Clements, H. A. " Operational Experience of the SSS (Synchro-Self-Shifting) Clutch Particularly in Naval Machinery ". *A.S.M.E.* 72–GT–81 *loc. cit.*— SSS Gears Ltd.

133. MAAG Synchronous Shifting Clutch.

Couplings

134. Brown T. W. F. " Developments in Marine Steam turbine design ". *Trans. I.E.S.* 1960–61, Vol. 104–3—Pametrada standard gear-tooth flexible coupling.

52. Young, I. T. Discussion on T. P. Jones paper. *Trans.I.Mar.E.* Vol. 84–15. 1972 *loc. cit.*—frictional torque introduced at gear-tooth couplings due to misalignment.

135. Young, I. T. Discussion on Hepper and Mudd paper. *I.M.A.S.* 1973.—vibration on high speed turbine—torque tube pinion line.

128. Crook, A. W. A.E.I. Turbine-Generator Engineering 1968. *Loc. cit.*—vibrations associated with the running line.

136. Goodwin, A. J. H. *Loc. cit.* " Naval Gearing Requirements ". 6th R.T.C. 1967—Gear tooth coupling failure.

137. Williamson,. L. " Survey of Flexible Couplings ". *Machine Design Engineering.* May 1965.

138. Lucas Aerospace Ltd. *Contoured Flexible Diaphragm Coupling (Bendix)*—maximum torque at inner diameter; ratio outside to inside diameters and thickness determine the flexibility.

139. Metastream—as above but using laminations pierced to form radial spokes.

140. Goody, E. W. Turboflex. Group discussion 1974. *Proc.I.Mech.E.*—Laminated metallic coupling with driving and driven attachment points on a common pitch circle diameter, where the torque is transmitted more or less by direct tension on the blades.

141. Wolff, P. H. W. " The Design of Flexible Disc Misalignment Couplings ". *Proc.I. Mech.E.* Applied Mechanics 1951–165.

142. Metropolitan-Vickers (G.E.C.) *Strain Gauge Tests on Flexible Disc Couplings 1945*; Metropolitan-Vickers (G.E.C.), *Use of Flexible Disc Couplings on Steam Turbine Locomotive 1930–1945.*

143. Charles, C. J. and Dawson, P. H. " Marine Turbine Propulsion Gearing—Foundations of a Current Design Philosophy ". *Proc.I.Mech.E.* 1970. Paper 17.—Full scale running tests on couplings under torque and misalignment.

66. Kerpestein, J. B. " Gear Transmission in the Euroline Class Vessels ". *M.E.R.* April 1973, *loc. cit.*—Use of Bendix flexible disc couplings.

144. Archer, S. " Marine propulsion, with Special Reference to the Transmission of Power "—36th Thomas Lowe Gray Lecture, *Proc.I.Mech.E.* 1964.—Excellent survey of couplings and clutches in marine use.

145. Stolzle, K. " Zahnkupplungen ". *Technische Mitteilungen* 1962.—Tooth couplings.

146. Stolze, K. and Hart, S. *Freilaufkupplungen*, Springer-Verlag. Berlin 1961.—Free-running couplings.

Conformal Teeth

147. Wildhaber, E. *Circular Arc Gears.* 1923. Also *Machinist*, 29 September 1945.

148. Walker, H. *An Analysis of Gear Tooth Profile for Helical Gears.* University of London Library 1940. Also *The Engineer*, 29 April 1960.

149. *Novikoff Gears—D.S.I.R.* Translation 1958.

150. Wells, C. F. and Shotter, B. A. " The Development of CirCarC Gearing ". *A.E.I.* Eng. 2 (2), p. 83.

151. Martin, A. C. " Westland Helicopter Lynx Engine—Conformal Tooth Form Gearing ". *Proc.I.Mech.E.* 1970.—Discussion.

GEAR DAMAGE
26. Dunlop, I. M. and Good, E. B. *loc. cit. Trans.I.Mar.E.* 1963.—Scuffing due to partial blocking of oil supply on gas turbine astern train. Fig. 23.1.
152. Shannon, J. F. " Section through Tooth ". *A.E.I. Engineering.* Marine Special issue 1963.—Section through worn tooth. Fig. 23.6.
153. Frederick, S. H. and Newman, A. D. *Proc.I.Mech.E.* 1958. Plate C. Fig. 23.2. Welding and tearing. Plate 6.a.
116. De Gruchy and Harrison—*loc. cit.* Fig. 23.3 (a) low speed scuff; (b) medium speed scuff; (c) high speed scuff; (d) initiation of scuff.
112. Chesters, *loc. cit. Proc.I.Mech.E.* 1958. Pit on through-hardened steel. Fig. 22.1a. Exfoliation on case-hardened steel. 1b.
24. Darlington, W. H. *loc. cit. Trans.I.Mar.E.* Fig. 23.5.
111. Cameron, A. and Newman, A. P. *loc cit.* Pametrada Conf. Fig. 23.7—path of crack in hardened and shaved pinion tooth (d). Cameron and Newman, Broken tooth on same pinion as tooth shown in (d) and exhibiting fatigue failure (e).
153. Frederick, S. H. and Newman, A. D. " Tooth Failure Influenced by Heavy Pitting ". *Proc.I.Mech.E.* 1958, p. 77, Plate 7. *Gear Failures.* Paper 13. Inter. Conf. on Gearing. *Proc.I.Mech.E.* 1958.

NOISE
154. King, A. J. *The Measurement and Suppression of Noise.* Chapman and Hall 1965. G.E.C.(U.K.) Acoustic Laboratories.
155. Dawson, P. H. and Tate, C. " A Modern Gear Test Rig—G.E.C.(U.K.) ". *Engineering* 1961.
156. Kohler, H. K., Pratt, A. and Thompson, A. M. " Dynamics and Noise of Parallel Axis Gears ". *Proc.I.Mech.E.* 1970. Paper No. 14. Also Paper 10—Munro, R. G. and Paper 16—Welbourn, D. B. on Gear Errors and their Resultant Noise Spectra.
157. Kohler, H. K. *Analysis of Measurements of Gear Noise and Vibration.* Conference on the recording and interpretation of measurements. Joint British Consm. for Stress Analysis, April 1972.
136. Goodwin, A. J. *loc. cit.* " Constant Position Mountings ". 6th R.T.C. on Marine Gearing 1967.
158. Lutje-Schipholt, R. M. " Marinization of Aero-Gas Turbines ". *Trans.I. Mar.E.* October 1975.—Alternative rubber pad mountings and cardan shaft connections with flexible couplings.
159. Sachs, R. M. " Description of Propulsion Systems for the DDH-280 Class Gas Turbine Destroyers ". *A.S.M.E.* 69-GT26. Figs. 2, 3 and 11.—Gas turbines and gears on raft, supported on rubber mounts, with nylon-rubber flexible output coupling.